STANDARD NOTATION

English Symbol	Units	Definition
ΔP	in. H_2O, in. Hg, lb/in.^{2}	Dynamic pressure ($q = .000492\ \sigma V^2 =$ in. H_2O), or a difference between two pressures.
ΔP_c	in. H_2O, in. Hg	Differential pressure, $q_c = q(1 + \frac{1}{4} M^2 + \cdots)$.
P_F	—	Full throttle altitude power factor.
PHP	550 ft lb/sec	Airplane parasite horsepower required.
P_i	lb in.^{2}, in. Hg	Measured tailpipe impact pressure.
P_{im}	lb/in.^{2}, in. Hg	Mean average tailpipe impact pressure.
$(\Delta P)_{pe}$	in. H_2O	Increment of static pressure position error in static pressure lines.
P_s	lb/in.^{2}	Tailpipe static pressure in jet propulsion equations.
$P_w\sqrt{\sigma}$	550 ft lb/sec	Universal power parameter $= BHP\sqrt{\sigma}/(W/W_s)^{3/2}$.
q	in. H_2O, lb/ft^2	Dynamic pressure (see ΔP).
q_c	in. H_2O, lb/ft^2	Differential pressure (see ΔP_c).
R	—	Geometrical wing aspect ratio $= b^2/S$; also W/W_s.
R	53.6 ft/°F	Gas constant for tailpipe exhaust gases.
R/C	ft/min	Rate of climb.
R/D	ft/min	Rate of descent.
RPM	1/min	Engine revolutions per minute.
R/R	deg/sec	Rate of roll.
$R_w\sqrt{\sigma}$	ft/min	Universal rate of climb parameter $= (R/C)\sqrt{\sigma}/(W/W_s)^{1/2}$.
S	ft^2	Wing area.
S	ft	Take-off distance.
t	sec, min, °C	Time or free air temperature.
T	°K (°R)	When used in equations for theory (ft-lb-sec-°F system) represents degrees Rankine (°F + 460). In all final equations converted to engineering units, T is in degrees Kelvin (°C + 273).
Δt	°C, min.	Temperature rise due to adiabatic compression; also time increment.
t_c	°C	Carburetor air temperature.
Δt_c	°C	Carburetor air temperature rise above free air temperature.
THP	550 ft lb/sec	Airplane thrust horsepower.
T_i	°R or °K	Measured tailpipe impact absolute temperature.
T_s	°R	Exhaust gas static absolute temperature.
T_T	°R	Tailpipe impact absolute temperature.
ΔT_V	°R	Temperature equivalent of velocity.
v	ft^3/lb	Specific volume of a gas.
V	mph (ft/sec)	*True airspeed:* When used in theory, units are ft/sec until converted to engineering units. Also impeller tip speed.
$V\sqrt{\sigma}$	mph	*Equivalent airspeed:* $V\sqrt{\sigma} = V_{cal} - \Delta V_c$.
V_c	mph	Velocity of sound: $V_c = 44.85\ \sqrt{T}$.
ΔV_c	mph	*Airspeed compressibility correction.* Increment of airspeed indicator reading due to compressibility.
V_{cal}	mph	*Calibration airspeed,* or the reading a perfect instrument in a perfect installation would have: $V_{cal} = V_m - \Delta V_{pe}$.
V_G	mph	Airplane ground velocity.
V_j	ft/sec	Exhaust gas jet velocity.
V_m	mph	*Measured airspeed;* that is, V_r corrected for instrument laboratory calibration error.
ΔV_{pe}	mph	*Airspeed position error* determined from airspeed position error calibration in flight.
V_r	mph	*Observed airspeed.* Airspeed indicator *reading* as observed from the instrument.
V_w	mph	Wind velocity; also airplane true airspeed corrected for gross weight variation; also airspeed corrected to a new gross weight.
$V_w\sqrt{\sigma}$	mph	Universal speed parameter $= V\sqrt{\sigma}/(W/W_s)^{1/2}$.
V_s	mph	$V/\sqrt{T/T_s} =$ standard airspeed for jet-propelled airplanes.
w	lb/ft^3	Weight density of air.
W	lb or lb/sec	Airplane gross weight or rate of weight flow of any fluid.
W_a	lb/sec	Weight flow of air.
W_f	lb/hr	Weight flow of fuel.
W_g	lb/sec	Weight flow of gases.
Y_a	—	Pressure ratio parameter $= (P_{im}/P)^{(\gamma-1)/\gamma} - 1$.
Y_A	—	Pressure ratio parameter $= (P_i/P)^{(\gamma-1)/\gamma} - 1$.
Y_b	—	Impact to static absolute tailpipe temperature ratio: $T_T/T_s = (P_{im}/P_s)^{(\gamma-1)/\gamma} - 1$.

See inside rear cover for Standard Notation on Greek symbols and on subscripts.

FLIGHT TESTING

CONVENTIONAL AND JET-PROPELLED AIRPLANES

THE MACMILLAN COMPANY
NEW YORK · BOSTON · CHICAGO
DALLAS · ATLANTA · SAN FRANCISCO

MACMILLAN AND CO., LIMITED
LONDON · BOMBAY · CALCUTTA
MADRAS · MELBOURNE

THE MACMILLAN COMPANY
OF CANADA, LIMITED
TORONTO

FLIGHT TESTING

CONVENTIONAL AND JET-PROPELLED AIRPLANES

By **BENSON HAMLIN, B.Ae.E., M.I.A.S.** PROJECT ENGINEER, FORMERLY
SENIOR FLIGHT RESEARCH ENGINEER, BELL AIRCRAFT CORPORATION, NIAGARA FALLS, NEW YORK

NEW YORK · THE MACMILLAN COMPANY · 1946

Previous edition entitled *Standard Flight Test
and Data Reduction Methods* copyrighted 1942 by
The Macmillan Company.

INTRODUCTION

The past fifteen years, including the turbulent, wartime years, have wrought great improvements in the exact science of flight testing. Its hazy aura of glamourous high adventure has been brought into sharper focus; a still hazardous and highly specialized profession has matured to its greater responsibilities of precise laboratory evaluation. It has, under the guidance of such leaders as the late, great, Edmund T. Allen, initiated an ever-growing literature of flight test techniques, procedures, and methods of interpretation of flight test data.

Despite the expanding wealth of flight test literature, however, the need has remained for a compilation under one cover of sufficient " know-how " to cover comprehensively so broad a subject. The necessity has been clear-cut for a detailed reference manual to guide the relatively inexperienced and to refresh the general practitioners of the engineering profession.

The Bell Aircraft Corporation, like many others in the industry, faced during the early years of this war, an acute shortage of skilled and trained flight test personnel. The rapid influx of relatively young and inexperienced engineers taxed severely that small nucleus in which was vested the specialized knowledge so essential to successful flight diagnosis. To meet this challenge there was inaugurated under Benson Hamlin a lecture training course from which has sprung this book.

Recognizing the obvious necessity for standardization of the many and often controversial methods of data analysis, he carefully prepared this material as a basis for unification of flight research activities and the reporting of results therefrom. An effort has also been made to eliminate much of the confusion heretofore fostered by misinterpretations of aeronautical terminology. The original manual enjoyed extensive distribution in this country, and the comments received provided the stimulus for publication.

Mr. Hamlin matriculated at the Rensselaer Polytechnic Institute from which he was graduated with honors in 1937. Subsequently, he was employed for more than three years in the Flight and Aerodynamic sections of United Aircraft Corporation. During the next two years he held a position of responsibility performing similar duties at Vega Aircraft Corporation, during which time he gained experience working and consulting with the Boeing Aircraft Company's Flight Test organization.

Since July of 1942 he has held the position of Senior Flight Research Engineer at Bell Aircraft Corporation.

In the main, Mr. Hamlin has relied heavily on the practical experiences of a number of organizations and agencies in his selection of the more practical and proven methods currently in use. Although it is difficult to encompass thoroughly so broad a field of endeavor, this basic material should provide a suitable foundation for further development of flight test science.

In addition to providing a practical handbook for the flight test engineer and the engineering test pilot, this book should prove a useful guide for the college student and those professions concerned with the use of or interpretation of flight test information.

ROBERT M. STANLEY, CHIEF ENGINEER
BELL AIRCRAFT CORPORATION

CONTENTS

PART ONE: CONVENTIONAL AIRPLANES

1. *General Order of Experimental Flight Testing* ... 1

2. *Basic Measurements* ... 3
   2.1 Altitude ... 3
   2.2 Wind Velocity ... 3
   2.3 Carburetor Air Temperature ... 4
   2.4 Atmospheric Density Ratio ... 4
   2.5 Laboratory Instrument Calibrations ... 4
   2.6 Engineering Units ... 4

3. *Bernoulli's Equation* ... 5
   3.1 Bernoulli's Equation for Incompressible Flow ... 5
   3.2 Bernoulli's Equation for Compressible Flow ... 6
   3.3 Fundamental Concepts Derived from Bernoulli's Equation ... 7
   3.4 Critical Mach Number of a Body ... 8

4. *Theory of Airspeed Measurement* ... 10
   4.1 Theory of the Airspeed Indicator ... 10
   4.2 Compressibility Increment Correction ... 11
   4.3 Airspeed Measurement Errors ... 13

5. *Airspeed and Altimeter Position Error Calibration* ... 15
   5.1 Altimeter Method ... 15
   5.2 Speed Course Method ... 20
   5.3 Trailing Bomb Method ... 22
   5.4 Airplane Pacing Method ... 23
   5.5 Effect of Gross Weight on Position Error ... 23
   5.6 Position Error Limitations ... 24

6. *Determination of Mach Number* ... 27
   6.1 Purpose of Mach Number Determination ... 27
   6.2 Derivation from Theory ... 27
   6.3 Graphical Solution ... 27

7. *Free Air Temperature Determination* ... 28
   7.1 Discussion ... 28
   7.2 Mach Number Effect on Temperature Measurement ... 29
   7.3 Free Air Pickup Calibration ... 30
   7.4 Graphical Solution ... 31

8. *True Airspeed Data Reduction* ... 32
   8.1 Discussion ... 32
   8.2 Method ... 32

9. *Stalling Speed* ... 43
   9.1 Discussion ... 43
   9.2 Data Reduction ... 43
   9.3 Data Required ... 44

10. *Engine and Power Characteristics* ... 45
    10.1 Theory of Power Curves ... 45
    10.2 Brake-Horsepower Determination from Power Curves ... 47
    10.3 Types of Power Curves ... 48
    10.4 Effect of Mixture on Power ... 50

11. *Critical Altitude Determination* ... 51
    11.1 Purpose and Definition of Critical Altitude ... 51
    11.2 Power Correction Method ... 51
    11.3 Determination of Temperature Exponent ... 52
    11.4 Data Reduction ... 58
    11.5 Data Required ... 59

12. *Universal Speed-Power Polar* ... 60
    12.1 Introduction ... 60
    12.2 Effect of Density on Power Required ... 60
    12.3 Effect of Gross Weight on Power Required ... 61
    12.4 Universal Speed-Power Polar ... 61
    12.5 Data Reduction ... 62
    12.6 Data Required ... 63

13. *Maximum Speed Determination* ... 64
    13.1 Discussion ... 64
    13.2 Universal Polar Method ... 65
    13.3 Conventional Polar Method ... 65
    13.4 Speed-Power Polar Data Reduction ... 66

14. *Climb Performance* ... 69
    14.1 Discussion ... 69
    14.2 Universal Rate-of-Climb-Speed Curve ... 71
    14.3 Density Altitude Method ... 72
    14.4 Data Reduction ... 75
    14.5 Data Required ... 75

15. *Take-Off and Landing Distances*   78
  15.1 Discussion   78
  15.2 Method for Ground-Run Distance   78
  15.3 Method for Air-Borne Distance   80
  15.4 Alternate Obstacle Distance Method   81
  15.5 Landing Roll Distance   81
  15.6 Data Reduction   81
  15.7 Data Required   81

16. *Range and Endurance*   83
  16.1 Discussion   83
  16.2 Method   83
  16.3 Data Reduction   86
  16.4 Data Required   86

17. *Stability and Control*   87
  17.1 Introduction   87
  17.2 Preliminary Stability and Control
       Check   91
  17.3 Longitudinal Static Stability in Linear
       Flight   92
  17.4 Longitudinal Static Stability in Acceler-
       ated Flight   94
  17.5 Rearward Center of Gravity for Neutral
       Longitudinal Stability   96
  17.6 Theoretical Considerations   97
  17.7 Forward Center of Gravity Limitation   97
  17.8 Directional Stability and Control   98
  17.9 Lateral Stability and Control   99

PART TWO: JET-PROPELLED AIRPLANES

18. *Turbo-Jet-Propulsion Engine Charac-
    teristics*   101
  18.1 Description of the Engine   101
  18.2 Advantages of Jet Propulsion   102
  18.3 The Nernst Cycle   103
  18.4 Dimensional Analysis of Engine Charac-
       teristics   103
  18.5 Engine Characteristics   106
  18.6 Tailpipe Thrust Determination   108
  18.7 General Remarks   112

19. *Concept of Thrust and Drag*   117
  19.1 Definition of the Forces Involved   117
  19.2 Proof of Ideal External Pressure Force 117
  19.3 Definition of Thrust and Drag   118
  19.4 Measurement of Drag in a Wind
       Tunnel   118

20. *Glide Polars*   119
  20.1 Purpose   119
  20.2 Method   119
  20.3 Data Reduction and Data Required   120

21. *Maximum Speed Determination*   122
  21.1 Discussion   122
  21.2 Method   122
  21.3 Gross Weight Correction   124
  21.4 Universal Speed-Thrust Polar   124

  21.5 Alternate Universal Method   125
  21.6 Data Reduction and Data Required   125

22. *Climb Performance*   127
  22.1 Discussion   127
  22.2 Method   127
  22.3 Universal Rate-of-Climb-Speed
       Curves   128
  22.4 Data Reduction and Data Required   128

23. *Take-Off and Landing*   131
  23.1 Method for Ground-Run Distance   131
  23.2 Method for Air-Borne Distance   131
  23.2 Landing Roll Distance   131
  23.4 Data Reduction and Data Required   131

24. *Range and Endurance*   133
  24.1 Discussion   133
  24.2 Method   133
  24.3 Data Reduction   135

Flight Test Report Outline   137

References   139

Centigrade-Fahrenheit Conversion Scales   140

Index   143

List of Symbols   end papers

USEFUL GRAPHS

FIGURE

4:2 Compressibility effect on airspeed indication 12

5:1 Slope of pressure altitude vs. pressure curve 16

5:2 Equivalent values of airspeed position error for static pressure position error 17

8:1 Mach number determination 33

8:2 Free air temperature and velocity of sound 38

8:3 Density ratio and density altitude 40

FIGURE

10:2 Engine power factor variation with altitude 46

11:1 Supercharger compression ratio variation with temperature 53

11:2 Brake horsepower temperature correction exponent n 56

18:12 Tailpipe jet thrust parameter 113

18:13 Tailpipe gas flow parameter 115

25:1 Centigrade-Fahrenheit conversion scales 140

Part One

Conventional Airplanes

BELL AIRCRAFT AIRPLANES IN FLIGHT

XP-77
P-39 AIRACOBRA
P-63 KINGCOBRA
P-59 AIRACOMET

CHAPTER 1

GENERAL ORDER OF EXPERIMENTAL FLIGHT TESTING

1.1 General Order of Experimental Flight Testing

Before an airplane is delivered to the flight research department, its various components, usually duplicate wings, tails, and other sub-assemblies, have been structurally tested by applying the design loads statically. After satisfactory completion of the tests, the airplane must be flown to demonstrate its flying characteristics, performance, and structural integrity. In general, the test program is conducted in the following order:

(a) Shakedown flights.
(b) Engine cooling and vibration.
(c) Stability check.
(d) Performance determination.

    (1) Airspeed and altimeter position error calibration.
    (2) Free air temperature calibration.
    (3) Stalling speeds.
    (4) Critical altitude.
    (5) Maximum level flight speed.
    (6) Saw-tooth climbs.
    (7) Climb to ceiling.
    (8) Take-off and landing.
    (9) Range and endurance.
    (10) Spins.
    (11) Dives.

(e) Final stability.
(f) Changes, redesign, service items, and miscellaneous.

The shakedown phase consists of pilot familiarization, functional check of all phases of operation, and a decision of the airworthiness of the aircraft from the standpoint of safety. An attempt is made to iron out the " bugs " and prepare the airplane for flight testing.

During shakedown the two critical items, engine cooling and vibration, are closely observed, and the following flights depend upon conditions encountered. Vibration must be satisfactory throughout the practical ranges of operation, and the engine must cool satisfactorily during ground operation, maximum power level flight, maximum power climb, and level flight cruising conditions at all altitudes. The cooling program is nearly always lengthy and complicated, and the requirements depend upon engine manufacturer and customer specifications. These tests often result in modifications to the airplane in order to comply with the specified requirements.

Stability check flights are made to establish the acceptability of the airplane, or to investigate any modifications necessary to make the airplane acceptable from the standpoint of safety, controllability, and maneuverability, as dictated by the customer. At this point, the airplane should be representative of its final configuration, and performance tests may be conducted in the hope that no more changes will be made which will necessitate redetermination of performance.

Determination of performance by flight testing is then undertaken for the purpose of demonstrating whether or not the airplane will meet the guaranteed performance, and of ascertaining the performance of which the airplane is capable and the method of operation required to produce these results. During flight testing, any limitations of the airplane are discovered and specified.

Since the atmospheric conditions are continually varying, the problem arises of reducing all performance to that which would be obtained under standard atmospheric conditions, as specified in reference 1[*] and adopted internationally. It is the primary purpose of this volume to standardize the methods of flight test data reduction to standard conditions. On this basis only, can the performance of airplanes be presented and compared.

Final stability tests are run to determine as

---

*List of references will be found in Appendix at end of this book.

completely as possible the limiting conditions under which dynamic stability exists and to what degree. Desired stability requirements depend upon the customer and the type of operation for which the airplane is intended.

The final phase of flight testing goes on as long as the airplane is in production, and even afterwards. Improvements, changes, compromises, service requirements, and adaptations continue to alter the airplane throughout its life.

In conclusion, it must be stated that this program of events is inevitably tempered by judgment, circumstances, conflicting requirements, weather, finances, time, manpower, other test programs, instrumentation, breakdown, safety requirements, and so on.

CHAPTER 2

BASIC MEASUREMENTS

2.1 Altitude

Absolute altitude refers to the vertical distance above sea level, that is, tapeline distance.

Pressure altitude refers to the absolute altitude in a standard atmosphere (reference 1) at which a given pressure is to be found. This is the altitude read by a standard altimeter when its zero setting is adjusted to the standard sea level pressure of 29.92 in. Hg (1,013 millibars). In all flight test work without exception, the altimeter is used to measure pressure altitude, and it is one of the first duties of the test pilot to verify this zero adjustment before take-off.

Density altitude refers to the absolute altitude in a standard atmosphere at which a given density is to be found. Density is determined by both the true air pressure (determined from the altimeter pressure altitude reading) and the true air temperature existing at a given flight test level.

Flight test pressure altitude readings must be corrected for " altimeter position error " as outlined in section 5.12, and air temperature readings for speed effect as given in Chapter 7.

Tapeline altitude is a more exact term for absolute altitude. Determination of tapeline altitude from pressure altitude and temperature is derived here as a basis for use in climb reduction.

The fundamental equation, upon which the complete derivation of the standard atmospheric values is based, is given in equation 3 of reference 1 as

$$dP = -g\rho dH \qquad (2:1)$$

This equation is derived as a summation of the vertical forces on a mass element of air as shown in Figure 2:1. Since the expression will be used for relatively small increments, it will be permissible to write the increment expression:

$$\Delta P = -g\rho\Delta H \qquad (2:2)$$

The altimeter is an absolute pressure gauge and is calibrated to read and indicate tapeline altitude

only in a standard atmosphere, that is, when the density is standard, or

$$\Delta P = -g\rho_s\Delta H_p \qquad (2:3)$$

For any set of conditions, equations 2:2 and 2:3 yield the same pressure increment, so they

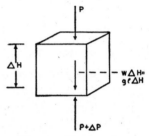

Fig. 2:1. Element of air

may be equated and a solution for tapeline altitude increment in terms of pressure altitude increment derived:

$$\Delta H = \Delta H_p \frac{\rho_s}{\rho} = \Delta H_p \frac{T}{T_s} \qquad (2:4)$$

Therefore, a pressure altitude increment, when multiplied by the ratio of the average actual to standard absolute air temperatures for that interval, will give the true tapeline altitude increment.

2.2 Wind Velocity

During take-off and landing tests, wind velocity measurement is required. An anemometer, which reads linearly in feet of airflow, and a stop watch are usually used near the ground. During such tests, wind velocity should be determined at not greater than ten-minute intervals, so that it may be plotted against time of day. From this curve the average wind velocity at any given time is determined. The air temperature in the shade also should be recorded.

2.3 Carburetor Air Temperature

For engine horsepower determination the carburetor air temperature must be recorded. Thermocouples on the carburetor air screen provide the most accurate measurement, and are used by the engine manufacturer on engine test stands. If the measurement in flight is made in the same manner as that used by the engine manufacturer during engine power determination for his power curves, no correction for air velocity, ram, or other factors should be made. Therefore, the actual carburetor air temperature measured is to be used with no further corrections.

The centigrade temperature scale has been adopted as standard throughout this book, and a centigrade-Fahrenheit conversion scale is provided at the end of the appendix.

2.4 Atmospheric Density Ratio

In reference 1, the National Advisory Committee for Aeronautics has derived a standard variation of atmospheric temperature and pressure, and hence density, with altitude, which has been adopted in the United States. All flight test performance is corrected to this standard as a basis for comparison. Density ratio is convenient to use instead of density, and is determined from the true atmospheric pressure and absolute temperature:

$$\sigma = \frac{\rho}{\rho_0} = \frac{PT_0}{P_0T} = \text{density ratio} \qquad (2:5)$$

where
$$P_0 = 29.92 \text{ in. Hg}$$
$$T_0 = 288° \text{ K}$$

2.5 Laboratory Instrument Calibrations

It is understood that all instrument readings must be corrected for the laboratory calibration error inherent in any instrument of measurement, although this is sometimes specifically mentioned. It is recommended that in flight test reports the original observed data and the measured readings be included in the data reduction tables and the instrument laboratory calibrations appear in the appendix. All calibrated instruments should bear the date and place of last calibration somewhere on the case at all times, and all instruments should be calibrated periodically, at not greater than three-month intervals.

Plotting of laboratory instrument calibration error versus instrument reading is adopted here as standard procedure. By definition this *calibration error* is determined by subtracting the true value from the instrument reading. Therefore, a true measurement value is obtained by the algebraic subtraction of the *calibration error* from the observed instrument reading. Subscript r denotes the observed or recorded instrument readings, while subscript m refers to a true measurement value, after correcting for calibration error.

2.6 Engineering Units

All equations in the discussion of theory are given in the English system (foot-pound-second-degrees Fahrenheit), while the final equations for actual use have been revised in terms of the appropriate engineering units as shown in the list of symbols found in the end papers.

CHAPTER 3

BERNOULLI'S EQUATION

3.1 Bernoulli's Equation for Incompressible Flow

All equations in this chapter are given in the foot-pound-second-degrees Fahrenheit system. Further information and discussion may be found in reference 5.

When a body moves through a fluid with uniform velocity V in a definite direction, the conditions of fluid flow are exactly the same as if the body were at rest in a uniform stream of velocity, V, and it is more convenient always to consider the latter viewpoint. Thus consider the airplane or pitot tube as stationary in the uniform field of fluid flow. If the fluid flow at any point is uniform, that is, the flow pattern and velocity remain constant in magnitude and direction with time, the flow is streamline flow. Streamlines may be drawn which represent the flow of the fluid elements, and, since the streamlines represent the direction of flow at all points along them, there is no flow across streamlines.

In such a steady flow, it is possible to obtain a simple relationship between the pressure and velocity at any and all points along a streamline. The dynamical equation of motion of a small element of fluid forming part of a stream tube defined by a small cylinder of streamlines shown in Figure 3:1 may be derived from Newton's

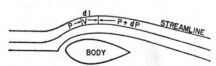

Fig. 3:1. Flow of streamlines around a body

second law of motion expressed by $F = Ma$. The mass of fluid in the element of cross-sectional area A and length dl is $M = \rho A dl$. The net force upstream acting on this cross-sectional area by virtue of the pressure difference is $F = -A dP$. The acceleration term may be expressed as

$$a = \frac{dV}{dt} = \frac{dl}{dt}\frac{dV}{dl} = V\frac{dV}{dl}$$

Substituting these values in the force equation gives

$$-A dP = \rho A dl V \frac{dV}{dl} \qquad (3:1)$$

which reduces to

$$VdV + \frac{dP}{\rho} = 0 \qquad (3:2)$$

This equation represents the dynamics of a minute incremental element along a streamline which, when integrated, may be applied to all elements throughout the streamline. Bernoulli's equation in its most elementary form becomes

$$\frac{V^2}{2} + \int \frac{dP}{\rho} = \text{constant} \qquad (3:3)$$

Equation 3:3 represents the true relationship of the three fundamental variables in any fluid streamline flow. Note that ρ may be a function of both pressure and temperature. The integration cannot be performed until the interdependency of mass density, ρ, and pressure, P, can be evaluated for the particular medium under consideration. If the fluid were incompressible, that is, that the mass density of the fluid will not change with changes of pressure, such as water, whose compression characteristics are negligible, then the density remains a constant value and the simple integration of equation 3:3 multiplied by ρ yields

$$P + \frac{\rho V^2}{2} = \text{constant} = P_1 + \frac{\rho V_1^2}{2} = \text{etc.} \quad (3:4)$$

This simple streamline flow equation is the basis of all hydraulics engineering. In the past this same equation also was used in aerodynamics because of its simplicity and because of the fact that up to speeds of $V\sqrt{\sigma} = 200$ mph and altitudes up to 15,000 feet, the compressible characteristics of air are small enough to be neglected.

It states that at any point along a streamline the sum of the static pressure and $(\frac{1}{2}) \rho V^2$ is equal to a constant value, which is called Bernoulli's constant, or the total pressure head of the fluid. Thus as the velocity increases along a streamline the static pressure decreases and vice versa. If the velocity is reduced to zero, then the static pressure has increased to the total pressure head, or the streamline constant. Thus if the total pressure is measured at a point in the streamline by stopping the fluid, and the static pressure of the moving fluid also is measured, then this difference in pressure makes it possible to calculate the velocity of the fluid. Since only the difference between these two pressures is required, a differential pressure gauge is most convenient, one side picking up pressure from a total head tube and the other side picking up pressure from a static tube. Such a pitot-static tube is shown in Figure 3:2.

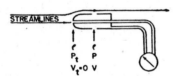

Fig. 3:2. Pitot-static tube

Bernoulli's constant is satisfied at both the total head and static openings since both points lie on identical streamlines. The density of the incompressible fluid remains unchanged, so equation 3:4 represents both cases as follows (where $V_t = 0$):

$$P_t + \frac{\rho V_t^2}{2} = P + \frac{\rho V^2}{2} = \text{constant} \quad (3:5)$$

$$\Delta P = P_t - P = \frac{\rho V^2}{2} = q = \text{dynamic pressure}$$
$$(3:6)$$

$$V = \sqrt{\frac{2\Delta P}{\rho}} \quad (3:7)$$

Obviously, the differential pressure gauge can be calibrated in terms of velocity *for a given density of the fluid*, and we have a velocity or speed indicator. In hydraulics ρ is constant, and this simple equation for velocity applies throughout.

As mentioned before, this incompressible relation was used in determining flight test speeds, in which case the density, which varies with altitude, was determined from pressure and temperature measurements of the air in flight. Since the error in assuming air to be incompressible can no longer be tolerated, it will not be developed further.

3.2 Bernoulli's Equation for Compressible Flow

Returning to Bernoulli's equation (3:3), we know that air is a compressible fluid and that its density will vary with changes in pressure. Since changes in pressure and velocity along streamline flow about a given body occur very rapidly, there is no exchange of heat between adjacent fluid elements, and the density is further affected by temperature changes as a consequence of pressure changes. Therefore, the pressure and density are related by the adiabatic law:

$$\frac{P}{P_t} = \left(\frac{\rho}{\rho_t}\right)^\gamma \quad (3:8)$$

where γ is the ratio of specific heat at constant pressure to that at constant volume. This value for air has been determined as 1.4 (see reference 1). The subscript $_t$ represents the conditions at any point, but for convenience is also the condition for stopped airflow. No subscript indicates free stream values. Substituting $\rho = (P/P_t)^{1/\gamma}\rho_t$ from equation 3:8 in equation 3:3, and integrating:

$$\frac{V^2}{2} + \frac{\gamma}{\gamma - 1} \frac{(P_t)^{1/\gamma}}{\rho_t} (P)^{(\gamma-1)/\gamma} = \text{constant} \quad (3:9)$$

Substituting $P^{1/\gamma}/\rho$ for $P_t^{1/\gamma}/\rho_t$ from equation 3:8:

$$\frac{V^2}{2} + \frac{\gamma}{\gamma - 1} \frac{P}{\rho} = \frac{V_t^2}{2} + \frac{\gamma}{\gamma - 1} \frac{P_t}{\rho_t} = \text{constant}$$
$$(3:10)$$

Equation 3:10 is the complete and accurate form of *Bernoulli's equation* as used in aerodynamics since it includes the effects of compressibility, and is, in fact, the basic foundation of this science. Airspeed measurement and effect of speed on temperature measurement, as well as many other problems, base their solutions on this expression. The limitations of this equation are stated in the definition of streamline flow. Behind a propeller, for example, energy has been added to the air, and if this flow is uniform or streamline flow at some distance behind the propeller, then the equation will apply. However, the total head, or Bernoulli's constant, will have a larger value aft of the propeller than ahead of it, and the above expression cannot equate the conditions of the one flow to the conditions of the other. Also, it should be remembered that Bernoulli's equation cannot be applied to conditions within the boundary layer, wake of a body, or turbulent flow where the flow pattern ceases to be laminar.

3.3 Fundamental Concepts Derived from Bernoulli's Equation

Many interesting facts may be derived from equations 3:8 and 3:10, knowing that the local speed of sound is expressed by

$$V_c = \sqrt{\frac{\gamma P}{\rho}} = \sqrt{\left(\frac{\gamma P_0}{\rho_0 T_0}\right) T} \qquad (3:11)$$

If free airstream flow is represented by the left side of equation 3:10 and stopped airflow, where $V_t = 0$, by the right side, then the true *differential pressure*, $P_t - P$, may be derived in terms of *dynamic pressure*, $(\frac{1}{2})\rho V^2$ or q, and Mach number, V/V_c or M:

$$\Delta P_c = P_t - P = q\left(1 + \frac{M^2}{4} + \frac{M^4}{40} + \cdots\right)$$
$$= \text{differential pressure} \qquad (3:12)$$

In fact, this equation shows how much the incompressible dynamic pressure of the fluid is increased by the compressibility characteristics, the factor being the quantity in parentheses.

In order to study the variation of cross-sectional area with velocity in streamline flow, the equation for continuity of flow, $\rho VA = $ constant, and Bernoulli's equation may be differentiated with respect to velocity and combined to give

$$\frac{dA}{dV} = -\frac{A}{V}(1 - M^2) \qquad (3:13)$$

This shows how a stream tube contracts in cross-sectional area as the velocity increases, if the local velocity is less than the local velocity of sound. However, when Mach number equals unity, the cross-sectional area has reached its minimum possible value, and as the Mach number increases further, the stream tube starts to expand again, as shown by Figure 3:3. As air flows around a body, its thickness causes the unobstructed area for flow to diminish until the point of maximum thickness of the body is reached, following which this area is again increased to its original value aft of the body. As a

result of the reciprocal relation between velocity and area, the flow conditions may be represented by a to b on the curve and from b back to a again. However, if the free stream velocity were high enough so that the speed of sound would be reached, $M = 1.0$, before the maximum thickness point on the body is reached, then with further

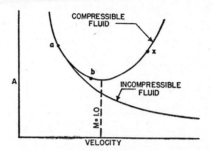

Fig. 3:3. Variation of cross-sectional area of a fluid with change in velocity

increase in velocity the streamlines want to expand. But, contrarily, the area available is still decreasing to this maximum thickness point, and the circumstances become contrary to the natural requirements of the fluid.

The reverse reasoning may also be used, assuming supersonic velocity at the minimum section around the body corresponding to point x on the curve. Going further aft along the body, the unobstructed area is expanding, yet for the initial velocity reduction the air seeks a smaller area. It follows that the flow pattern about a body must change very considerably as the velocity approaches and exceeds the velocity of sound. A compressibility shock wave is the consequence.

It is interesting to note that this equation may be used in the design of convergent-divergent nozzles to obtain supersonic velocities, and the equation shows why the nozzle must be expanded beyond the critical or minimum throat diameter at which point the velocity of sound obtains. However, if such a nozzle is cut off at the throat, a convergent nozzle, the issuing jet will "explode" into the atmosphere, resulting in an inefficient jet whose velocity will not exceed the local velocity of sound. Thus the atmosphere refuses to permit its particles to travel faster than the velocity of sound (the velocity of propagation of a pressure wave transmitted from particle to particle), unless carefully controlled artificially. If this control is applied or exists inefficiently, tremendous energy will be required to overcome the natural restraint. The problem is one in which a fluid under artificial or confined flow can be properly controlled to yield supersonic velocities, but in the final analysis, when exhausted to surrounding atmosphere, the atmospheric particles will not exceed sonic velocity, at which point air begins to assume the characteristics of a solid.

Once a Mach number of 1.0 has been reached and a shock wave forms, the adiabatic relationship between pressure and density (equation 3:8) is no longer true and Bernoulli's equation as derived will not apply.

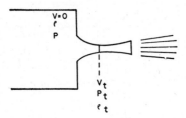

Fig. 3:4. Nozzle flow conditions

In order to investigate the conditions at the throat of a nozzle attached to a chamber of compressed air (Figure 3:4), Bernoulli's equation is again used. Since the throat velocity has already been shown to equal the local velocity of sound, substitute for this V_t^2 term its equal $\gamma P_t/\rho_t$ in the right side of equation 3:10. The left side will represent the chamber conditions where $V = 0$:

$$\frac{\gamma}{\gamma - 1}\frac{P}{\rho} = \frac{1}{2}\frac{\gamma P_t}{\rho_t} + \frac{\gamma}{\gamma - 1}\frac{P_t}{\rho_t} \quad (3{:}14)$$

From this and equation 3:8, the following relations may be derived:

$$\frac{P_t}{P} = \left(\frac{2}{\gamma + 1}\right)^{\gamma/(\gamma-1)} = .528 \text{ for } \gamma = 1.40 \quad (3{:}15)$$

$$\frac{\rho_t}{\rho} = \left(\frac{2}{\gamma + 1}\right)^{1/(\gamma-1)} = .634 \text{ for } \gamma = 1.40 \quad (3{:}16)$$

$$\frac{V_{ct}}{V_c} = \left(\frac{2}{\gamma + 1}\right)^{1/2} = .912 \text{ for } \gamma = 1.40 \quad (3{:}17)$$

Thus, the throat static pressure for sonic velocity is about half the chamber pressure and the mass discharge flow is thus limited. This is so for a convergent or a convergent-divergent nozzle. The latter nozzle can expand the throat pressure down to the exhausting pressure and create supersonic speeds. For such a nozzle properly designed, shock waves will occur only at the exit, but if the ratio of exhausting pressure to chamber pressure is greater than that for which the nozzle was

designed (but less than .528), then shock waves will form in the divergent part of the nozzle.

3.4 Critical Mach Number of a Body

The foregoing discussion has brought out the fact that a shock wave will be formed when the local velocity of the air reaches sonic velocity, unless in carefully confined flow. As the velocity along streamlines passing around a body increases, the static pressure decreases. Thus it is possible to relate the velocity of sound along a streamline to the static pressure at which it occurs. Taking Bernoulli's equation and writing the left side for free airstream conditions, the right side represents the flow at some point x around the body, say where the maximum negative pressure exists. We may define Mach number of the body as the ratio of the free airstream velocity approaching the body divided by the velocity of sound in the free air. We are solving for the condition that the local velocity at point x is equal to the local velocity of sound, $V_{c_x}^2 = \gamma P_x/\rho_x$, so the equation is written

$$\frac{V^2}{2} + \frac{V_c^2}{\gamma - 1} = \frac{\gamma P_x}{2\rho_x} + \frac{\gamma}{\gamma - 1}\frac{P_x}{\rho_x} \quad (3{:}18)$$

from which it is possible to derive the final equation, using the adiabatic relationship of equation 3:8 and dividing by q:

$$\frac{\Delta P}{q} = \frac{P_x - P}{q}$$
$$= \frac{2}{\gamma M_{cr}^2}\left[\left\{\frac{(\gamma - 1)M_{cr}^2 + 2}{\gamma + 1}\right\}^{\gamma/(\gamma-1)} - 1\right] \quad (3{:}19)$$

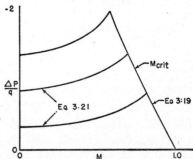

Fig. 3:5. Pressure coefficient variation with Mach number and critical limit

The plot of this equation is shown in Figure 3:5. It shows that for any given Mach number, sonic velocity will obtain if the negative pressure difference (static pressure at the given point below that of the free airstream) becomes as large as that shown on the curve. Conversely, if the pressure at any point on the body becomes as low as shown by the curve, sonic velocity has been reached, and the body has reached its critical Mach number.

This curve is useful in the determination of the critical Mach number of a body from pressure distribution measurements in a wind tunnel, such

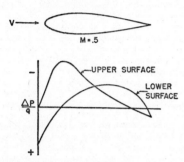

Fig. 3:6. Variation of pressure distribution over an airfoil

as shown in Figure 3:6. Since such high Mach numbers are not usually attainable, tests may be made at several lower speeds to define the parameter curves shown. According to Glauert's and Prandtl's theory, this variation should be

$$\frac{\Delta P}{q} = \frac{(\Delta P/q) \text{ at } M = 0}{\sqrt{1 - M^2}} \qquad (3:20)$$

By test, this variation has been found to underestimate the variation of pressure coefficient with Mach number, and von Karman in reference 16 has derived the more accurate expression

$$\frac{\Delta P}{q} =$$

$$\frac{(\Delta P/q)_{M=0}}{\sqrt{1 - M^2} + [M^2(\Delta P/q)_{M=0}/2(1 + \sqrt{1 - M^2})]}$$
$$(3:21)$$

Thus it is possible to find the maximum negative value of the pressure coefficient from pressure distribution tests about a body at a given Mach number and extrapolate the results for Mach number by this equation. The point at which this curve intersects that for critical Mach number as plotted in Figure 3:5 will represent the Mach number at which a compressibility shock wave may be expected to occur for the body at the attitude under consideration.

It should be noted that although theory indicates that a shock wave should occur at the critical Mach number, as shown, there are considerable test data showing the critical Mach number to be greater than that expected in some cases and lower in others. However, the analysis given indicates how a body may be evaluated in terms of its susceptibility to the onset of compressibility effects by pressure distribution studies well below the critical Mach number.

These ramifications have been given merely to help appreciate the significance of Bernoulli's equation, upon which the theory of airspeed measurement and other developments to follow are based.

CHAPTER 4

THEORY OF AIRSPEED MEASUREMENT

4.1 Theory of the Airspeed Indicator

Bernoulli's equation for a compressible fluid, derived in Chapter 3 and copied from equation 3:10, is

$$\frac{V^2}{2} + \frac{\gamma P}{(\gamma - 1)\rho} = \frac{V_t^2}{2} + \frac{\gamma P_t}{(\gamma - 1)\rho_t} = \text{constant} \tag{4:1}$$

As written, the equation is applied to the conditions obtained at the two orifices of a pitot-static head used for airspeed measurement. The left side of the equation represents the free air conditions along a streamline, and these are the conditions which do exist at the static orifices of a pitot-static head, which has no position error, that is, in a perfect installation. The right side of

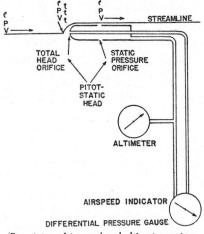

Fig. 4:1. Airspeed and altimeter system

the equation represents the conditions at the pitot orifice of the pitot-static head, where the velocity, V_t, is zero and consequently the pressure is the *total* or stopped pressure, being the sum of the static (atmospheric) pressure and the differential (impact) pressure. These conditions are represented in Figure 4:1.

The difference between the total pressure, P_t, and the static pressure, P, from equation 4:1, making use of equation 3:8, is

$$\Delta P_c = P_t - P$$

$$= P\left[\left\{1 + (\gamma - 1)\frac{\rho V^2}{2\gamma P}\right\}^{\gamma/(\gamma-1)} - 1\right] = q_c$$

$$= \textit{differential pressure} \tag{4:2}$$

Solving equation 4:2 for V and multiplying both sides by $\sqrt{\sigma}$ gives

$$V\sqrt{\sigma} = \sqrt{\frac{2\gamma P}{(\gamma - 1)\rho_0}\left\{\left(\frac{\Delta P_c}{P} + 1\right)^{(\gamma-1)/\gamma} - 1\right\}} \tag{4:3}$$

Equation 4:3 reveals the possibility of using a differential pressure gauge to detect the differential pressure, ΔP_c, existing between the pitot-static head orifices as shown in Figure 4:1, and then graduating the dial in speed instead of pressure units. However, P, the static pressure, which is the atmospheric pressure, is also a variable in equation 4:3. This means that a different scale graduation on the dial of the airspeed indicator would be required at every individual pressure altitude in order to read the true value of $V\sqrt{\sigma}$ directly from the instrument at every pressure altitude. A multitude of scales is obviously impractical, and the scale corresponding to standard sea level pressure altitude was adopted in 1925 by the U. S. Army and Navy (reference 4). All airspeed indicators are calibrated by the values from this formula at sea level as set forth in this reference. The adopted standard reading* of an

---

*The airspeed indicator is purely and simply a differential pressure gauge in its own right, measuring the differential pressure given by equation 4:2, arising by virtue of the unique pressure change characteristics wrought by stopping a moving fluid. Calibrating this gauge in fallacious speed units serves no particularly beneficial purpose other than conformation with a conventional manner of thinking. This fictitious calibration was initiated in the middle twenties when most aircraft flew so slow and low that the rule of thumb of 2 per cent increase in observed speed per 1000 feet to estimate true airspeed was sufficiently rigorous. However, within the past decade of greatly increased performance, and from this time on, as long as pressure instruments are used to measure air velocity, it should be borne in mind that no matter in what units the dial of the pressure meter is calibrated, true speed will still have to be computed through at least eight successive operations; this will become apparent in the succeeding chapters.

airspeed indicator is hereby defined as the calibration airspeed, V_{cal}, which is expressed by equation 4:3 at sea level pressure as

$$V_{cal} = V \sqrt{\sigma_0}$$

$$= \sqrt{\frac{2\gamma P_0}{(\gamma-1)\rho_0}\left\{\left(\frac{\Delta P_c}{P_0}+1\right)^{(\gamma-1)/\gamma}-1\right\}}$$

$$= C_1 \sqrt{\left(\frac{\Delta P_c}{C_2}+1\right)^{2/7}-1} \qquad (4:4)$$

The term $V\sqrt{\sigma_0}$ is included to stress the fact that V_{cal} is equal to this quantity only for the unique value of $\sigma = 1.0$. This equation is the basis for the calibration of airspeed indicators in the United States. Tabulated values may be found in reference 4.

Referring back to the incompressible equation (3:6), the difference between the total and static pressure would be

$$\Delta P = P_t - P = \frac{\rho V^2}{2} = q = dynamic\ pressure$$

$$(4:5)$$

This quantity referred to as the *dynamic pressure*, or velocity pressure, is in fact the kinetic energy of a unit volume of free air, and is not to be confused with the differential pressure as expressed in equation 4:2. *Impact pressure* is the total pressure, static plus differential pressure, as defined in reference 15 and contrary to its usage in reference 4.

Again solving for V and multiplying by $\sqrt{\sigma}$

$$V\sqrt{\sigma} = \sqrt{\frac{2(\Delta P)}{\rho_0}} \qquad (4:6)$$

This quantity, which for the *incompressible case* is independent of altitude, has been erroneously referred to as " indicated airspeed," whereas the quantity that an airspeed indicator indicates has already been derived in equation 4:4 and defined as calibration airspeed in order to avoid confusion. For $V\sqrt{\sigma}$ less than 200 mph and altitudes below 15,000 feet the resulting error is small, but as modern aircraft are exceeding the values that have been quoted by a considerable margin, this assumption may no longer be tolerated.

$V\sqrt{\sigma}$ is properly a direct measure of the kinetic energy of any given volume, Q, of *moving* fluid:

$$kinetic\ energy = \frac{MV^2}{2} = \frac{Q\rho_0(V\sqrt{\sigma})^2}{2} \qquad (4:7)$$

However, $V\sqrt{\sigma}$ is defined as *equivalent airspeed* for two reasons: First, this speed value appears in all of our coefficients such as lift, drag, and moment. Except for Mach number effects such coefficients will remain constant for constant equivalent airspeeds. Second, this terminology has already been used to some extent.

4.2 Compressibility Increment Correction

It is now obvious that the dial reading of an airspeed indicator must be corrected in order to find $V\sqrt{\sigma}$, from which the true airspeed, V, is to be obtained. The correction may take the form of a multiplication factor, Ω, which would be equation 4:3 divided by equation 4:4:

$$\Omega = \frac{V\sqrt{\sigma}}{V_{cal}} = \sqrt{\frac{P[(\Delta P_c/P+1)^{(\gamma-1)/\gamma}-1]}{P_0[(\Delta P/P_0+1)^{(\gamma-1)/\gamma}-1]}}$$

$$(4:8)$$

A table of calculated values for Ω is found in reference 7.

The equation relating equivalent and calibration airspeeds may be derived from the same equations:

$$V\sqrt{\sigma} =$$

$$1701\sqrt{\frac{P}{P_0}\left\{\left(\frac{[1+\frac{1}{5}(V_{cal}/761)^2]^{3.5}-1}{P/P_0}+1\right)^{1/3.5}-1\right\}}$$

$$(4:9)$$

Here the value of the constants ($\gamma = 1.40$) have been included, leaving the fundamental variables: equivalent and calibration airspeeds and altitude pressure ratio.

Either equation is cumbersome and will yield the same final results. In data reduction, it is more convenient to find $V\sqrt{\sigma}$ by subtracting the proper increment from V_{cal}, and this increment is defined as the compressibility correction, ΔV_c. Then $V\sqrt{\sigma} = V_{cal} - \Delta V_c$ and ΔV_c for various values of V_{cal} and pressure altitude, as obtained from equations 4:8 or 4:9, is plotted in Figure 4:2.

In order to appreciate the magnitude of the compressibility correction and the various definitions of airspeed previously given, Table 1 should be studied.

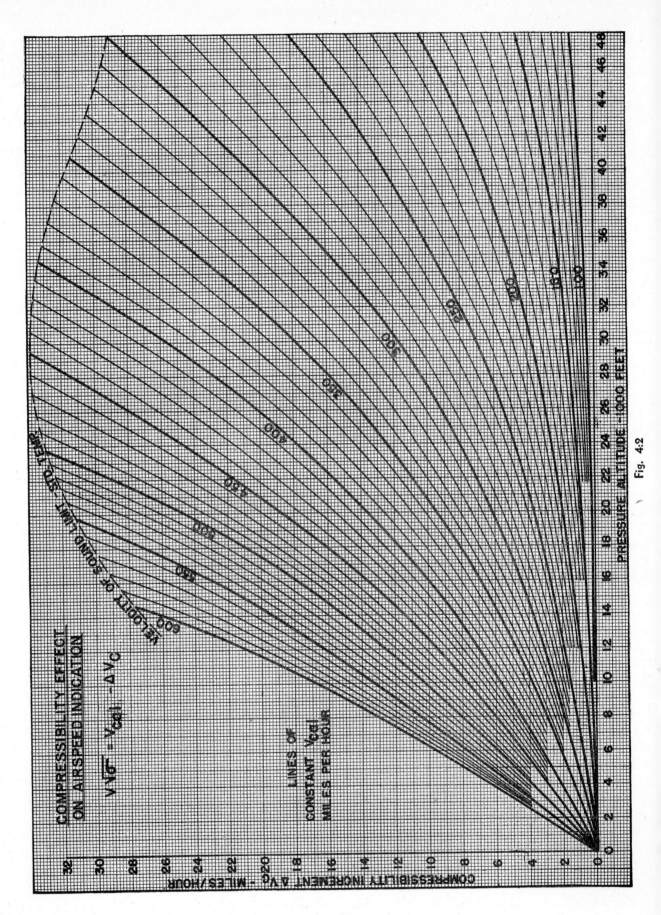

COMPRESSIBILITY EFFECT ON AIRSPEED INDICATION

$V\sqrt{\sigma} = V_{cal} - \Delta V_c$

LINES OF CONSTANT V_{cal}
MILES PER HOUR

COMPRESSIBILITY INCREMENT ΔV_c — MILES/HOUR

PRESSURE ALTITUDE — 1000 FEET

VELOCITY OF SOUND-TIME STD. TEMP.

Fig. 4.2

12

TABLE 1. EFFECT OF COMPRESSIBILITY AND DENSITY ON TRUE AIRSPEED DETERMINATION

Calibration airspeed: V_{cal}, mph	300	300	300	300	288.2	150
Pressure altitude: H_p, ft	0	10,000	30,000	30,000	30,000	40,000
Compressibility correction: ΔV_c, mph	0	2.5	11.8	11.8	10.3	3
Equivalent airspeed: $V\sqrt{\sigma}$, mph	300	297.5	288.2	288.2	277.9	147
Free air temperature: t, °C	15	−5	−44	−24	−24	−55
Density ratio: σ	1.00	.738	.374	.343	.343	.245
True airspeed: V, mph	300	346	471	492	474	296.5

4.3 Airspeed Measurement Errors

Airspeed is measured universally by means of the pitot-static head mounted in the airstream, with the pitot and static pressure lines connected to an airspeed indicator, which is simply a very sensitive *differential pressure* gauge calibrated as described by equation 4:4.

This system is subject to the following errors and effects:

(a) Instrument laboratory calibration error.
(b) Position error.
　(1) Pitot-static head form error.
　(2) Pitot-static head location error.
(c) Error due to dynamic unbalance.
(d) Acceleration error.
(e) Compressibility correction.

Error (a) is simply the laboratory calibration error inherent in any instrument of measurement. It is determined by comparing the instrument readings for accurately measured differential

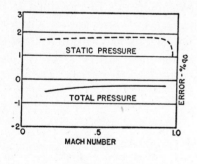

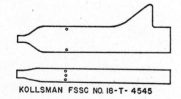

KOLLSMAN FSSC NO. 18-T-4545

Fig. 4:3.　Kollsman airspeed head

pressures applied in the laboratory in accordance with the standard airspeed calibration values adopted as given in reference 4. Modern sensitive airspeed indicators are very accurate by virtue

of careful design for low friction and for temperature compensation.

Error (1) in position error in the subcritical flow region may arise from the shape of the pitot-static head and the location of the static holes on the head. (See Figures 4:3 and 4:4.) However, in the modern design of pitot-static heads, this error has been practically eliminated when the head is

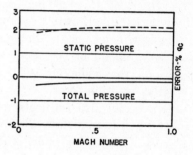

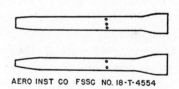

AERO INST CO FSSC NO. 18-T-4554

Fig. 4:4.　Aero airspeed head.

not yawed more than 8 to 10 degrees. Up to sonic velocity, the correct total head pressure is transmitted by the pitot orifice, but beyond a Mach number of .7 or .8 the pressure at the static orifices may begin to depart appreciably from the correct static pressure. At the present time the latter error is becoming a vital problem, and a discussion of it may be found in reference 3.

Error (2) in position error arises from the fact that the pitot-static head mounted on the airplane must necessarily be located in the disturbed pressure field created by the motion of the airplane. This phenomenon is considered as affecting only the static pressure at the unique location, that is, position of the static orifices, since, by Bernoulli's equation, the total head at any point on a streamline remains constant.

Figure 4:5 shows the contours of constant static pressures about an airfoil, those ahead and behind showing higher than free airstream, and the others lower. The pitot tube will measure the actual

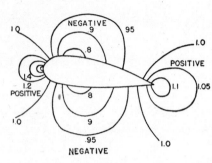

Fig. 4:5.   Static pressure field around an airfoil

velocities by virtue of the varying static pressures, although, as mentioned previously, the total head is everywhere constant along a streamline. A pitot tube ahead of the wing will have negative position error, while one below the wing will show positive position error.

This disturbed air also subjects the fixed pitot-static head to yawed airflow. *Position error, or airspeed system installation error, is defined as the combination of the pitot-static head form error (b)(1), and the location error (b)(2), and must be determined by flight test.* Chapter 5 is concerned with the determination of this error.

Error (c) occurs only during changes in pressure altitude, during which the *change* in atmospheric pressure must be transmitted through both the pitot and the static lines to be cancelled out at the airspeed indicator. This requires air to flow in both lines. However, standard airspeed installations always have had a static line system volume (altimeter and rate of climb indicators are connected only to the static line) several times greater than that of the pitot line systems. It is therefore evident that the transmission of the change in atmospheric pressure will have a greater lag in the static than in the pitot line. Thus, the differential pressure at the airspeed indicator will not be purely the differential pressure due to the airspeed, upon which airspeed measurement is based. Such a system is dynamically unbalanced. This error may be determined experimentally as in reference 2, but is more simply accounted for in section 5.3.

Error (d) occurs because of the lag in transmission (as mentioned in the previous paragraph and in reference 2) of the changing total head pressure due to changing airspeed during acceleration or deceleration. In the past, flight testing has not been concerned with accurate speed measurements during appreciably accelerated flight conditions and therefore this error will not be considered further.

In special cases of accelerated flight conditions the instruments themselves will be affected by g's since the internal gears and linkages are not statically balanced.

Effect (e) should not be classified as an error and has been accurately accounted for in the theory of aerodynamics (section 4.2) as the compressibility increment correction.

CHAPTER 5

AIRSPEED AND ALTIMETER POSITION ERROR CALIBRATION

5.1 Altimeter Method

5.11 Theory

The definition and discussion of position error in section 4.3 leads to the logical conclusion that position error is almost entirely the result of the existence of an erroneous pressure at the static orifices of the pitot-static head mounted on the airplane. Actually, substantial angles of yaw will produce errors at both the pitot and static orifices, but a properly installed head is so mounted that the maximum angle of yaw of the head throughout the normal flight range is held to a minimum. That is, the pitot-static head is mounted at an angle of attack to the airflow which is approximately halfway between the airflow direction at the head existing at maximum and stalling speeds. On standard installations, the yaw angle at the stalling speed is greatest and the error due to yaw may be appreciable.

The altimeter method of determining position error is based on this consideration and consists of the use of two altimeters, which are absolute pressure gauges, to measure this error in static pressure. One altimeter is used to measure the true atmospheric pressure by an observer on a tower. The other altimeter, which is already connected to the static line in the airplane, is read in conjunction with the airspeed indicator by the pilot as the ship passes the tower level. This method makes it impossible to obtain points close to the stalling speed for obvious reasons of safety.

Possible errors (c) and (d) in section 4.3 dictate the requirement of a long approach to the tower at tower level and at a stabilized speed. Consequently, a tower on top of a small hill would be an ideal location.

5.12 Method

Essentially, the difference between the two altimeter readings determines the pressure differ-ence between that at the static orifices and that of the free air. Both altimeters must be accurately calibrated over the small range for which they will be used and both should be set at 29.92 in. Hg. Also, both altimeters should be read together on the ground before and after the flight to make sure they both give the same results. The differential pressure existing at the pitot-static head and recorded by the airspeed indicator, is then adjusted for this static pressure error, and the correct airspeed reading, V_{cal}, determined. Position error is recorded as the difference between the measured airspeed indicator reading, V_m, and the correct reading, V_{cal}.

In translating the difference in altimeter readings in feet, into the difference in pressure, the slope of the pressure versus pressure altitude curve is required. Below the isothermal region the altimeter calibration is expressed in reference 1 by

$$\left(\frac{P}{P_0}\right)^{.19} = \left(1 - \frac{aH_p}{T_0}\right) \qquad (5:1)$$

The solution for the slope is

$$\frac{dP}{dH_p} = -\frac{(P/P_0)^{.81}}{67.4} = \text{in. } H_2O/\text{ft for } H_p$$

$$< 35,332 \text{ ft} \qquad (5:2)$$

Above the isothermal level, the slope (from equations 4 and 6a of reference 1) is

$$\frac{dP}{dH_p} = -\frac{(P/P_0)}{51.4} = \text{in. } H_2O/\text{ft for } H_p$$

$$> 35,332 \text{ ft} \qquad (5:3)$$

These slopes and their reciprocals are plotted against true pressure altitude in Figure 5:1. Then for any H_p the value of dP/dH_p may be

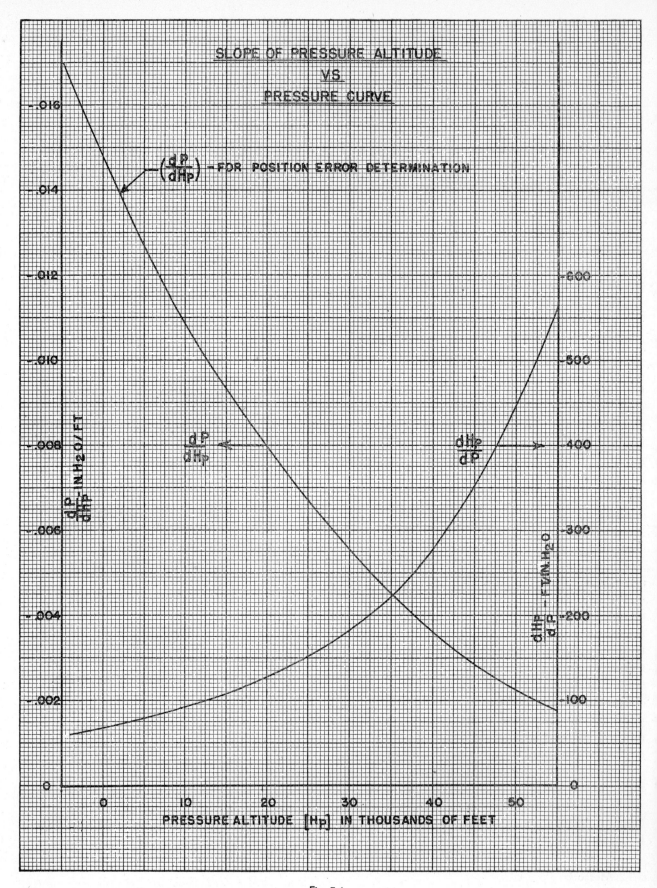

Fig. 5:1

16

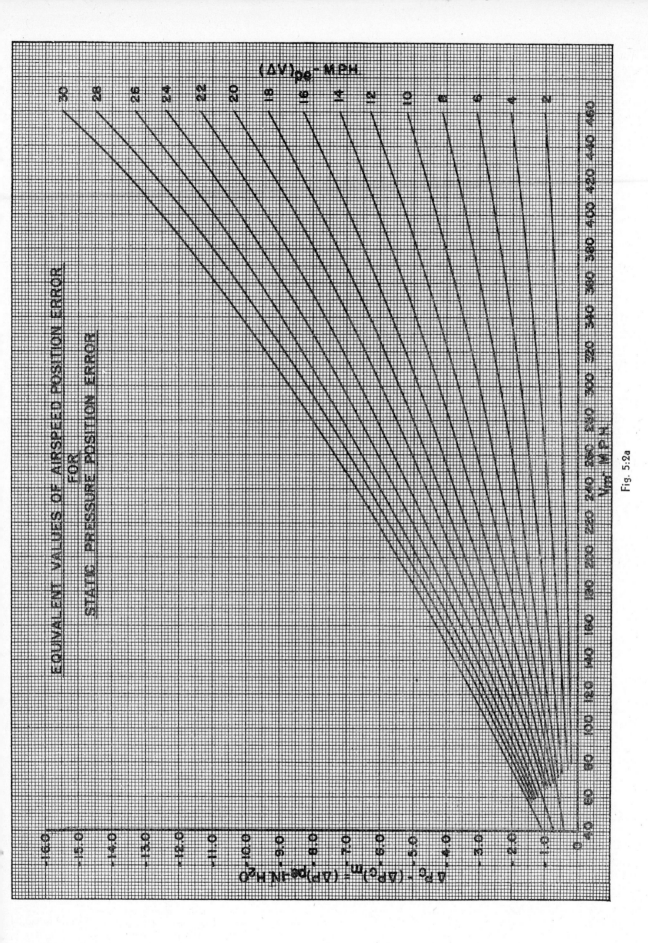

EQUIVALENT VALUES OF AIRSPEED POSITION ERROR
FOR
STATIC PRESSURE POSITION ERROR

$(\Delta V)_{pe}$ - MPH

$\Delta P_C - (\Delta P_C)_m = (\Delta P)_{pe}$ IN H_2O

V_{ic} MPH

Fig. 5:2a

17

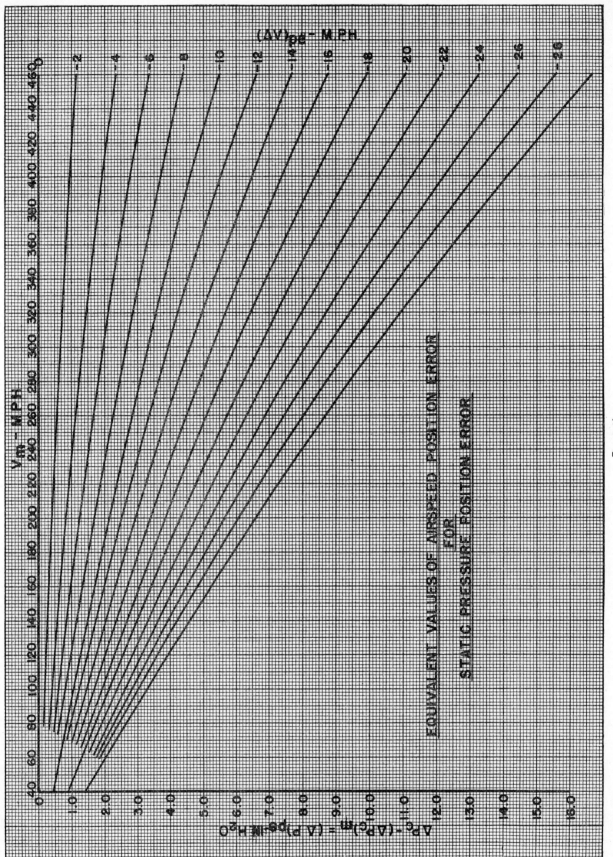

EQUIVALENT VALUES OF AIRSPEED POSITION ERROR
FOR
STATIC PRESSURE POSITION ERROR

Fig. 5:2b

18

read from this figure and the static pressure position error determined by

$$(\Delta P)_{pe} = [(H_p)_m - H_p] \frac{dP}{dH_p} = \Delta H_p \left(\frac{dP}{dH_p}\right) \tag{5:4}$$

So the true static pressure at the static orifices is

$$P = P_m - (\Delta P)_{pe} \tag{5:5}$$

and therefore the true differential pressure should be (see equation 4:2)

$$\Delta P_c = P_t - P = P_t - [P_m - (\Delta P)_{pe}]$$

$$= (P_t - P_m) + (\Delta P)_{pe} = (\Delta P_c)_m + (\Delta P)_{pe} \tag{5:6}$$

From reference 4, the standard values of differential pressure, ΔP_c, versus V_{cal} may be plotted, and from this curve airspeed position error may be determined as follows:

(a) For V_m airspeed measured, read the measured differential pressure, $(\Delta P_c)_m$, this represents.

(b) Add the static pressure position error to the measured differential pressure in order to obtain the true value of differential pressure that a perfect installation would have (according to equation 5:6).

(c) Read the true value of speed, V_{cal}, from the curve for the true value of differential pressure, ΔP_c.

(d) Subtract the true from the measured airspeed readings to obtain the airspeed position error:

$$(\Delta V)_{pe} = V_m - V_{cal} \tag{5:7}$$

In order to eliminate the preceding operations, the same method has been used to obtain the general curve plotted in Figures 5:2a and 5:2b. $(\Delta V)_{pe}$ may be read directly from the curve for the values of V_m and $(\Delta P)_{pe}$.

5.13 Effect of Altitude on Airspeed and Altimeter Position Error

Since the position error is an angle of attack (or speed) effect, it can be assumed* that $(\Delta P)_{pe}/\Delta P_c = (\Delta V)_{pe}/V_{cal}$ is valid at any altitude.

---

*The error of this assumption is discussed in reference 7 under "Effect of Compressibility on Position Error," and also in section 5.6, but will be neglected until further data become available.

This assumes that angle of attack, of which airspeed position error is a direct function, depends directly on V_{cal}. Therefore, $(\Delta P)_{pe}$ and $(\Delta V)_{pe}$ for a constant value of V_{cal} are the same at any altitude, but the altimeter position error, $(\Delta H_p)_{pe}$, will increase with altitude because the slope value of pressure altitude versus pressure, dH_p/dP, increases (see Figure 5:1). This altimeter position error variation must be accounted for, and the method is outlined at the end of section 5.14.

5.14 Data Reduction

It is important to record the average gross weight during airspeed position error calibration tests in order to take into account position error variation with gross weight as outlined in section 5.5.

Assume the following data for one test point:

$H_p = 800$ ft — true pressure altitude observed at the tower.

$V_m = 200$ mph — airspeed reading measurement (that is, V_r corrected for calibration error).

$(H_p)_m = 600$ ft — pressure altitude measurement by airplane altimeter (corrected for calibration error).

Data reduction is executed as follows:

(a) For $H_p = 800$ ft, $dP/dH_p = -.0144$ in. H_2O/ft from Figure 5:1.

(b) $(\Delta H_p)_{pe} = (H_p)_m - H_p = 600 - 800 = -200$ ft = altimeter position error at test altitude $H_p = 800$ ft.

(c) $(\Delta P)_{pe} = (\Delta H_p)_{pe} (dP/dH_p) = (-200)(-.0144) = +2.88$ in. H_2O = position error expressed as the error in static pressure at the static pressure orifices.

(d) For (c) and $V_m = 200$ mph, read $(\Delta V)_{pe} = -13.5$ mph from Figure 5:2b.

(e) Plot $(\Delta V)_{pe}$ versus V_m for the test points obtained and label the curve for the given airplane installation and the gross weight of test as shown in Figure 5:3. It is also very desirable to sketch the pitot-static head installation on the position error curve for reference purposes and to eliminate possible confusion with other such curves.

(f) The altimeter position error is then most easily redetermined by converting the faired $(\Delta V)_{pe}$ values into $(\Delta H_p)_{pe}$ values by the variation of dH_p/dP with altitude from Figure 5:1.

Calculations for $V_m = 200$ mph are illustrated in table 2. The final results are indicated by Figure 5:3.

TABLE 2. ALTIMETER POSITION ERROR
VARIATION WITH ALTITUDE

$(\Delta V)_{pe}$	$(\Delta P)_{pe}$	Altitude	dH_p/dP	$(\Delta H_p)_{pe}$
−13.5	+2.88	sea level	−67.6	−195
−13.5	+2.88	10,000	−92.5	−276
−13.5	+2.88	20,000	−126.0	−363
−13.5	+2.88	30,000	−181	−521

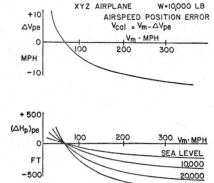

Fig. 5:3. Typical airspeed and altimeter position error curves

5.15 Supplementary Data

Since low-speed values close to the ground cannot be obtained, the low-speed calibration can be obtained at a reasonable altitude by resorting to the use of another airplane for reference. The latter airplane should be flown at a constant low speed, so that its position error variation with speed is not introduced in the data, and at a constant altimeter reading. The subject airplane should fly by the reference airplane for at least one speed already calibrated by the tower method and then successively lower speeds down to the stall. This merely insures that the test airplane is being calibrated at some constant pressure altitude which can be determined from the test airplane altimeter for a speed at which its calibration was already determined. This altitude, then, is the reference altitude datum for the lower-speed calibration runs. This method is recommended only as a very rough check since minute differences in the static pressure position error, which are difficult to measure accurately, result in large airspeed position errors (see Figure 5:2). There is no substitute for the trailing bomb method described in section 5.3 for determining stalling speeds.

5.16 Data Required

Average weight ⎫
Tower $(H_p)_r$ ⎪
Tower t_r ⎬ For each run at not greater
Airplane $(H_p)_r$ ⎪ than 20 mph increments
Airplane V_r ⎪ between minimum and maximum speeds.
Airplane t_r ⎭

The observer on the tower should estimate the difference in altitude between the airplane and tower levels if the pilot happens to be flying a little too high or too low.

Free air temperature should be recorded if convenient as these data can be used in calibrating the temperature pickup for the effect of airspeed as described in Chapter 6.

5.2 Speed Course Method
5.21 Theory

The object of this method is to fly the airplane near the ground over an accurately known ground distance, and by timing the run the true ground speed is determined. Then, by the theory of airspeed measurement, the true speed and density at which the run is made are converted to the proper value, V_{cal}, that a perfect airspeed installation system would read. The discrepancy between this value and that actually measured by the airplane airspeed indicator, V_m, is termed the airspeed position error.

Speed courses vary in length from 1 to 5 miles, but must be located in a vicinity where the course may be approached at a constant altitude. It must be stressed that speed course runs must be made in very smooth air and when there is little wind. Generally, good conditions exist only early in the morning. Also, in order to avoid " ground effect," the minimum altitude should not be less than one wing span.

In order to eliminate the effect of wind, a run must be made in each direction at the same airspeed reading. The airplane must also be flown with its longitudinal axis parallel to the speed course, as shown in Figure 5:4. This makes wind direction irrelevant, so its direction need not be accounted for in reducing the data. As a result, a cross wind will blow the airplane across the course, but the time interval in crossing the starting and finishing lines will be independent of the direction of the wind.

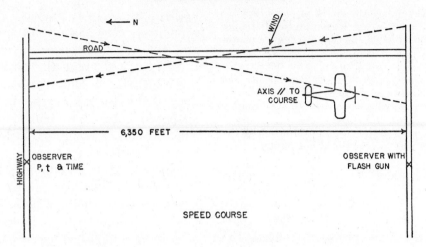

Fig. 5:4. Speed course for airspeed calibration tests

5.22 Method

To obtain one airspeed position error calibration point, two successive runs in opposite directions over the speed course are made at a constant airspeed reading, as close to one wing span above the land or water surface as safety permits. Between consecutive runs, the throttle should not be touched. The surveyed speed course length and measured time intervals to pass over the course determine the true ground speed in each direction. Averaging these two ground speeds cancels the effect of wind and gives the true airspeed. Knowing the air temperature and pressure altitude at the airplane elevation, the air density ratio, σ, is calculated. Then $V\sqrt{\sigma}$ is calculated. Referring to Figure 4:2, the difference between $V\sqrt{\sigma}$ and V_{cal} is negligible (unless the speed course were on a mountain in which case ΔV_c from this curve may be added to $V\sqrt{\sigma}$ with negligible error), and they are assumed equal. Position error is then

$$(\Delta V)_{pe} = V_m - V_{cal}$$

5.23 Data Reduction

Assume the speed course length to be 6,350 ft running north and south. The airplane is flown over the course in both directions at a constant airspeed indicator reading of 193 mph, taking 21.3 sec going south and 19.9 sec going north. Pressure altitude is 900 ft, air temperature 18° C and all instrument readings have been corrected for laboratory calibration errors.

(a) Ground speed, $V_g = 6,350/(1.467)$ (sec)
$= 4,330/\text{sec} = \text{mph}$

$$\text{N–S } V_g = 4,330/21.3 = 203 \text{ mph}$$
$$\text{S–N } V_g = 4,330/19.9 = \underline{217} \text{ mph}$$
$$2\,V = \overline{420} \text{ mph}$$
$$V = 210 \text{ mph}$$

(b) $\sigma = (P/P_0)(T_0/T) = (.9679)(288/291) = .956$.

(c) $V_{cal} = V\sqrt{\sigma} = 210\sqrt{.956} = 205 \text{ mph}$

(d) $(\Delta V)_{pe} = V_m - V_{cal} = 193 - 205 = -12$ mph

(e) Plot the position error curve of $(\Delta V)_{pe}$ versus V_m with a sketch of the pitot-static tube, noting the gross weight. (See Figure 5:3.)

(f) Determine the altimeter position error curve as outlined in step (f) of section 5.14.

5.24 Data Required

Average weight.

H_p — Pressure altitude.
t — Free air temperature.

Surveyed speed course length.

V_r (V_r in about 20 mph increments from minimum to maximum speed and time for consecutive runs in each direction at same V_r).

Δt — Time increment.
t_r — Airplane free air temperature.

Notes: Pressure altitude and air temperature should be measured by ground observers and, if necessary, corrected to the elevation at which the airplane is flown. Timing of the runs by observation from the ground or airplane depends for accuracy and safety upon the circumstances. If timing from the airplane is inadvisable, the flash of a camera photo-flash bulb may be employed at one end of the speed course to signal to the timers at the opposite end of the speed course the instant the airplane passes over this fixed point. The airplane instrument pressure altitudes should also be recorded, if possible, as they will afford a check by the altimeter method.

The temperature data are for use in calibration of the free air temperature pickup as outlined in Chapter 6.

5.3 Trailing Bomb Method

5.31 Theory

Since position error results from the airflow disturbance at the fixed pitot-static head, the trailing bomb is used as a method of eliminating this difficulty by suspending the head below the airplane. A trailing bomb should be suspended from the aft fuselage on a cable that is longer than the airplane wing span, and it will trail in a region where the static pressure of the air is least affected by the motion of the airplane. Careful design of the bomb and cable are required in order to avoid unstable oscillations, a good design being satisfactory up to a calibration airspeed of 300 mph.

It is standard practice to mount the static pressure head on the trailing bomb and to mount the total head pressure tube on the airplane with a vane and swivel joint so that it will always point into the relative airflow. Bernoulli's equation expressly states that the total head at any point along a streamline is constant. As long as the total head tube is located in streamline airflow and is not yawed to the airflow, it will be subjected to the true total pressure. The static tube is located in the undisturbed air below, and, since the weight of the air column in the line leading to the airplane compensates for the elevation difference between the static head and the airplane, transmits the correct static pressure to the airspeed indicator. This swiveling total head and static trailing bomb system will then obtain the proper differential pressure and the corresponding correct calibration airspeed. Among the disadvantages of locating the total head tube on the trailing bomb are the following:

(a) Two pressure lines are required, increasing the size and maintenance difficulties of the cable, and increasing the possibility of developing leaks in the lines, especially at the swiveling joint at the bomb.

(b) The recorded pressure at the total head would have errors as a result of (1) possible wind gradient, (2) slight error in total head pressure caused by a different air density below the airplane, (3) slightly different bomb speed in curvilinear flight near stalling speeds, and (4) unsteady airspeed readings from bomb swinging and gusts. The diagram of Figure 5:5 includes the elements of a trailing bomb system.

Since the trailing bomb may be used in glides, it affords an excellent means for accurate determination of stalling speeds. For this purpose, however, it must be dynamically balanced. This is easily accomplished experimentally by putting both the total head and static orifices in a common chamber and varying the pressure in the chamber at a rate corresponding to a 2,000 to 3,000 feet-per-minute rate of descent. Various volumes are inserted in the total head line until the airspeed indicator has no tendency to move in either direction from zero during the simulated rate of descent. This method results in approximately the same volume in both systems, and for the same size tubing the Reynolds number of the flow through both lines will be the same. Such a balancing volume is indicated in Figure 5:5.

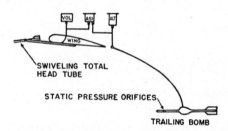

Fig. 5:5.   Trailing bomb airspeed calibrating system

All standard airplane airspeed systems are dynamically unbalanced, mainly attributable to the number of instruments connected only to the static lines. The error resulting is determined by the difference between the airspeed position error calibrations, as determined by the dynamically balanced trailing bomb method in level flight and in glide. When using the trailing bomb only in level flight, dynamic balance is not necessary.

It is standard practice to obtain position error curves for the various possible airplane configurations, gear up and down and flaps up and down, which may alter the pressure field at the airplane pitot-static head and thereby the position error. It is also customary to make power-off glide calibrations at steady airspeeds and to obtain the power-off stalling speeds with the bomb.

5.32 Method

Since the trailing bomb system is considered to be practically free from errors, the airspeed indicator reading from this system, corrected of course for any laboratory calibration error, is the true calibration airspeed, V_{cal}. Then $(\Delta V)_{pe} = V_m - V_{cal}$. Likewise, comparison of the airplane and static bomb altimeters determines the altimeter position error at the test pressure altitude.

5.33 Data Reduction

Assuming the following test results in level flight:

	Airplane system	Trailing bomb system
Airspeed indicator	180	190
Altimeter	10,325	10,500

$(\Delta V)_{pe} = V_m - V_{cal} = 180 - 190 = -10$ mph.

$(\Delta H_p)_{pe} = (H_p)_m - H_p = 10,325 - 10,500 =$
$$-175 \text{ ft at } H_p = 10,500 \text{ ft}$$

The altimeter position error curve may be determined as outlined in step (f) of section 5.14, and compared to the values actually determined by the altimeters. The preceding altimeter error at sea level can be determined as follows:

From Figure 5:1: dP/dH_p at sea level = $-.0147$ and at 10,500 ft = $-.0107$. The ratio of the slope at sea level to that at altitude is $(-.0147)/(-.0107) = 1.37$. Therefore, at sea level

$$(\Delta H_p)_{pe} = \left(\frac{-175}{1.37}\right) = -128 \text{ ft at sea level.}$$

This value checks the airspeed position error since

$$(\Delta P)_{pe} = (-175)(-.0107)$$
$$= (-128)(-.0147) = +1.88 \text{ in. H}_2\text{O}$$

At $V_m = 180$ mph and $(\Delta P)_{pe} = +1.88$ in. H$_2$O, $(\Delta V)_{pe} = -10$ mph, from Figure 5:2b.

Position error curves are plotted as before. (See Figure 5:3.)

5.34 Data Required

Average weight.

Airplane V_r. (Increments of airplane V_r of 10 or 20 mph between maximum and minimum speeds desired.)

Airplane $(H_p)_r$.

Bomb V_r.

Bomb $(H_p)_r$.

The following different runs may be made in both level flight and in glide. In the latter case, altimeter readings cannot be correlated and only one altimeter need be read.

Run	Landing flaps	Landing gear
A	Up	Up
B	Up	Down
C	Down	Down
D	Down	Up

When determining power-off stalling speeds, some intermediate landing flap settings should be tested; refer to stalling speeds, Chapter 9.

5.4 Airplane Pacing Method

The airplane pacing method is preferred by some, but is indirect in that the pacing airplane must have been calibrated by one of the previous methods. An airplane which has a known airspeed position error calibration is flown in formation adjacent to the airplane being tested. By comparison of the airspeed readings of both airplanes, the position error for the test airplane is determined. Data reduction will be similar to the trailing bomb method (section 5.3), obtaining the true values from the known position error curves of the given airplane. To be effective, this method requires reliable interplane communication.

5.5 Effect of Gross Weight on Position Error

5.51 Theory

Having determined the position error for the gross weight at which the airplane was flown, position error curves for various gross weights may be determined by calculation.

It has been shown in the preceding paragraphs that position error is a function of the pressure field, or pressure distribution, created by the motion of the airplane. Pressure distribution tests reveal that for reasonable variations in speed, $\Delta P/q$ remains constant at any point around a body, when its angle of attack, or attitude, is fixed. Since the attitude of an airplane is a direct function of lift coefficient, C_L, a plot of $\Delta P/q$ of a given point around the airplane versus C_L is independent of speed. Therefore, a plot of

$(\Delta P)_{pe}/\Delta P_c = (\Delta V)_{pe}/V_{cal}$ versus C_L will represent the fundamental relationship between the position error effect and the airplane-airspeed-system combination. Consequently, a substantial change in gross weight will result in a slight shift of the original position error curve.

The line of reasoning is as follows: If the gross weight is increased, the airplane speed must be increased to maintain a constant C_L (constant angle of attack), and the same ratio of airspeed position error to speed, $(\Delta V)_{pe}/V_{cal}$. Consequently, for the greater speed, $(\Delta V)_{pe}$ will be larger.

5.52 Data Reduction

Given: Airspeed position error curve as shown in Figure 5:6.

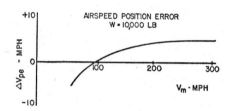

Fig. 5:6.   Airspeed position error curve

Required: Position error curve for 12,000 lb.
Solution:

(a) Calculate values of C_L for values of $(\Delta V)_{pe}/V_{cal}$ from the given airspeed position error curve, Figure 5:6, as shown in Table 3, where $C_L{}^* = 391 W_1/S(V_{cal})^2$ $W_1 = 10,000$ lb.

TABLE 3.   AIRSPEED POSITION ERROR RATIO AND LIFT COEFFICIENT CALCULATIONS

V_m	$(\Delta V)_{pe}$	V_{cal}	$(\Delta V)_{pe}/V_{cal}$	C_L
80	−10	90	−.111	1.28
164	+ 4	160	+.0025	.40
246	+ 6	240	+.0025	.20

(b) Plot $(\Delta V)_{pe}/V_{cal}$ versus C_L as shown in Figure 5:7.

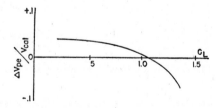

Fig. 5:7.   Airspeed position error ratio versus airplane lift coefficient

*Lift coefficients should be calculated on the basis of equivalent airspeed, $V\sqrt{\sigma}$. However, the extra complication is not warranted here.

(c) Calculate $(\Delta V)_{pe}$ versus V_m from (b) for $W_2 = 12,000$ lb, as shown in Table 4.

TABLE 4.   AIRSPEED POSITION ERROR CALCULATIONS FOR 12,000 LB GROSS WEIGHT

V_{cal}	C_L	$(\Delta V)_{pe}/V_{cal}$	$(\Delta V)_{pe}$	V_m
98.5	1.28	−.111	−10.9	87.6
175	.40	+.0025	+4.4	179.4
263	.20	+.0025	+6.6	269.6

where $C_L = 391 W_2/S(V_{cal})^2$ $W_2 = 12,000$ lb

The values given were chosen to illustrate that $(\Delta V)_{pe}$ at the same angle of attack will vary with gross weight. Even values of V_{cal} are normally chosen.

(d) Replot the new airspeed position error curve for the new gross weight as indicated in Figure 5:8.

In general, for airplanes whose gross weight variation is of the order of 10 per cent this gross weight effect may be neglected. Also, this gross

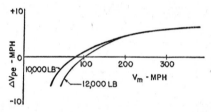

Fig. 5:8.   Airspeed position error curves at different gross weights

weight correction occurs only where the position error curve slopes, that is, the position error, varies with speed, and is generally significant only at the lower speeds.

If the airspeed position error is appreciably affected by gross weight, then the altimeter position error curves also will change. The latter curve may be arrived at by using the new airspeed position error curves and working backward through Figures 5:1 and 5:2. The airspeed position error and sea level altimeter position error curves should always cross-check each other.

5.6 Position Error Limitations

5.61 Effect of Altitude on Position Error

Position error is ascribable to the fact that the static pressure at the pitot-static tube is different from that of the free airstream because of local induced airflow changes in the fluid passing around the body. These airflow changes vary only with angle of attack or attitude of a body, or, in other words, are constant only for a constant attitude of the body. In the case of a wing, this attitude is defined by lift coefficient expressed by the following (which is not strictly true for large Mach number variations):

$$C_L = \frac{391\,W}{S(V\sqrt{\sigma})^2} \qquad (5{:}8)$$

Thus, " equivalent " airspeed defines " equivalent," or constant, angle of attack, at which position error remains constant. However, we have plotted position error versus measured airspeed, which is different from $V\sqrt{\sigma}$ by the compressibility correction, ΔV_c, and the position error, ΔV_{pe}. If ΔV_c did not change with altitude, no error would be made in using the curve as drawn, but Figure 4:2 shows that ΔV_c does vary with altitude. This means that a given V_m at low and at high altitudes really defines different values of equivalent airspeed and therefore different position errors, but in section 5.13 this discrepancy is neglected. At the present time, the magnitude of this error is of no great concern. This error is a function of the magnitude of the position error, and the best way to avoid it is to determine a location of the pitot-static tube to give the least possible position error. This is one valid reason for going to the trouble of investigating locations in order to find one having the minimum possible position error.

An English paper by Cameron (reference 17) shows how this error may be accounted for in a simple manner. After accurately evaluating this phenomenon mathematically, he shows how a simple approximation will give within ½ per cent of the true airspeed answer. This consists of evaluating the compressibility correction from a fictitious calibration airspeed equal to the measured airspeed minus *two* times the position error as we use it, as illustrated in Table 5.

TABLE 5. FREE AIRSPEED DETERMINATION

	Present method	Cameron method
V_m	320	320
H_p	30,000	30,000
$(\Delta V)_{\text{pe}}$	+30	+30
V_{cal}	290	
$V_m - 2(\Delta V)_{\text{pe}}$		260
ΔV_c	10.6	7.8
$V\sqrt{\sigma}$	279.4	282.2
V	456	460.6 within ½%
Error	4.6 mph approx.	

5.62 Effect of Mach Number on Position Error

The preceding error is an indirect result of Mach number, that is, brought about by the method of speed measurement in that equivalent airspeed cannot be measured directly. The effect discussed here is a direct Mach number effect on the pitot-static head itself, which, although previously suspected, is being currently investigated. The only flight test results known to the author have been made at Chance Vought. Two airspeed heads were located on the same airplane, one on a boom ahead of the wing and the other beneath the wing. At low altitudes, the difference

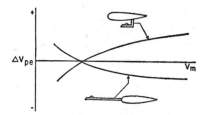

Fig. 5:9.   Position error curves for two airspeed head locations on wing

in the two airspeed indicator readings was plotted against the reading of one of them, and then the same data were obtained at a higher altitude. The results appeared as shown in Figures 5:9 and 5:10.

The two airspeed installations selected have position errors opposite in sign. If there were no effects of Mach number, the difference between the two readings at a given airspeed reading of one of them would remain constant. However, as

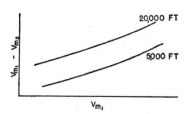

Fig. 5:10.   Illustration of position error variation with altitude and, therefore, Mach number

illustrated in Figure 5:10, there was considerable variation with altitude. It is logical to assume from the results that the Mach number effect is such as to increase the magnitude of the position error for each installation regardless of sign. However, from the results, the effect of Mach number is revealed qualitatively but not quantitatively since the effect on either installation cannot be separately evaluated.

Further investigation of this phenomenon is in progress, but again the desirability of determining an airspeed head location for zero or minimum position error is indicated.

5.63 Effect of Acceleration on Instruments

The majority of flight testing is done in un-accelerated flight, but for special tests, such as dive pullouts and windup turns for stability tests in accelerated flight, the effect of acceleration on instrument readings must not be overlooked. At the present time most instruments, including the airspeed indicator, are not balanced.

Calibration is accomplished by means of a centrifuge, or whirling arm, on which the instru-ments may be mounted. Pressures are applied to the instruments at $1\,g$ to obtain basic readings, and then observations are made at several different acceleration values. For instance, at $8\,g$, sensitive airspeed indicators have been observed to have an error of 15 to 20 mph and altimeters an error of about 300 feet.

These errors caused by acceleration may be plotted in a manner similar to that used for position error, except that these will be parameters of acceleration. For data reduction the basic instrument reading is determined by first correcting the observed values according to the accelerometer reading by using these calibration curves. Having determined the corresponding $1\,g$ values, data reduction then follows the standard methods.

CHAPTER 6

DETERMINATION OF MACH NUMBER

6.1 Purpose of Mach Number Determination

Mach number, the ratio of the true velocity of the air, or fluid, to the velocity of sound in that air, has been discussed in Chapter 3. Its significance related to compressibility effects has been emphasized, showing that when its local value is unity, that is, the velocity of sound actually obtains in the fluid, the streamline flow will begin to break down. However, it is much easier to determine the Mach number of the free airstream, and, since it is related to the local Mach number at any point of flow about a body at a given altitude by Bernoulli's equation, we usually speak of the Mach number of the air in which the body is operating and determine the critical Mach number for any specific body as its free air value when the local value at some point on the body is unity.

Here we are concerned merely with evaluating the free air Mach number in flight from the airspeed indicator and the altimeter readings. Having evaluated M, a solution for true airspeed becomes evident when it is known that the velocity of sound is a function of the temperature of the air. This principle is employed in the determination of true airspeed developed in Chapter 8.

6.2 Derivation from Theory

Again starting with Bernoulli's equation (3:10) for a compressible fluid:

$$\frac{V^2}{2} + \frac{\gamma}{\gamma - 1} \frac{P}{\rho} = \frac{V_t^2}{2} + \frac{\gamma}{\gamma - 1} \frac{P_t}{\rho_t}$$

The left side of the equation represents the free air conditions of velocity, pressure, and density. Although these conditions do not occur exactly at the static orifices of the pitot-static tube, we know, from Chapter 5, how to make the necessary corrections to the airspeed indicator and altimeter readings in order to obtain the correct free air values. The right side of the equation

represents the total head stopped flow condition at the pitot orifice, where $V_t = 0$ and the pressure and density values have both increased. If we divide the equation by $\gamma P / \rho = V_c^2$, (free air values), substitute M^2 for V^2 / V_c^2, and then $(P/P_t)^{1/\gamma}$ for ρ / ρ_t, the result is:

$$\frac{1}{2} M^2 + \frac{1}{\gamma - 1} = \frac{1}{\gamma - 1} \frac{P_t}{\rho_t} \frac{\rho}{P} = \frac{1}{\gamma - 1} \left(\frac{P_t}{P}\right)^{(\gamma-1)/\gamma}$$

Since $\quad \dfrac{P_t}{P} = \left(\dfrac{P_t - P}{P} + 1\right) = \left(\dfrac{\Delta P_c}{P} + 1\right)$

$$M = \sqrt{\frac{2}{\gamma - 1}\left[\left(\frac{\Delta P_c}{P} + 1\right)^{(\gamma-1)/\gamma} - 1\right]}$$

Evaluating $\gamma = 1.40$ for air (reference 1)

$$M = \sqrt{5\left[\left(\frac{\Delta P_c}{P} + 1\right)^{2/7} - 1\right]} \qquad (6:1)$$

In this expression ΔP_c is obtainable from the calibration airspeed from flight data, V_{cal}, by the adopted standard values found in reference 4. The value P is the true atmospheric static pressure obtained after correcting the altimeter data for position error and referring to reference 1 for the adopted standard values of atmospheric pressure. Mach number is thus a function of the ratio of the differential pressure to the atmospheric pressure.

6.3 Graphical Solution

For convenience in reading Mach number directly from values of calibration airspeed and pressure altitude, the curves of Fig. 8:1a through 8:1e have been drawn. (See pages 33–37.) A table for the solution of equation 6:1 may be found in reference 18, which was used in constructing these curves.

As an illustration, entering the figure for a calibration airspeed, V_{cal}, of 300 mph and a pressure altitude, H_p, of 20,000 feet, the Mach number, M, is equal to .570.

CHAPTER 7

FREE AIR TEMPERATURE DETERMINATION

7.1 Discussion

Temperature is perhaps the most difficult quantity to measure, and the human body and mind are not sensitive to small changes of its stimulus. We can perceive length, weight, force,

Fig. 7:1.   Bare thermocouple $K \equiv .75$

or time much more clearly than we can temperature. The determination of temperature is extremely important in flight testing as it affects primarily engine power, atmospheric density and

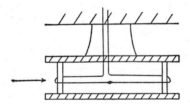

Fig. 7:2.   Lewis thermocouple $K \equiv .55$

thus airplane drag, true airspeed evaluation, and the velocity of sound. In attempting to measure temperature, errors may arise from conditions of radiation, conduction, convection, humidity,

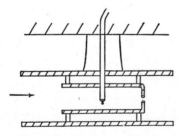

Fig. 7:3.   Shielded total head thermocouple $K \equiv 1.0$

pressure, friction, and variable temperature distribution in any given medium.

Of the several methods used to measure temperature, only the electrical resistance type

pickup with a millivoltmeter type indicator and the thermocouple type pickup using a nul-type potentiometer indicator are commonly employed in flight testing. The latter is preferred from the

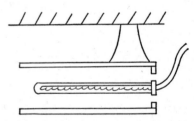

Fig. 7:4.   Lewis electrical resistance $K \equiv .75$

standpoint of accuracy and response characteristics but is objectionable from the size, weight, and complication standpoint, particularly in single place aircraft.

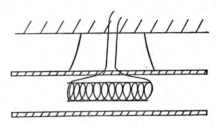

Fig. 7:5.   Weston electrical resistance $K \equiv .85$

At present there is no standardization of pickups used, and the importance of accuracy of measurement cannot be overemphasized. Figures

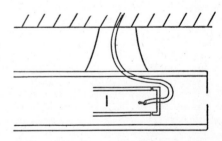

Fig. 7:6.   Proposed pickup $K \equiv 1.0$

7:1-7:6 illustrate several types of pickups in use, any of which may be developed for either instrument system mentioned.

7.2 Mach Number Effect on Temperature Measurement

As discussed in deriving Bernoulli's equation in Chapter 3, when air is stopped, the pressure rises. Also, with increase in pressure there is a consequent increase in temperature according to the thermodynamic characteristics of an adiabatic compression. It is impossible to place a temperature pickup in a moving airstream without bringing the air to rest at least at the front of the pickup, and there the temperature will be higher than that of the free airstream. At other portions of the pickup, the air velocities will be vastly different, causing variable temperatures around the surfaces of the pickup. There is no way to calculate the average effect except that its maximum value for stopped airflow from Bernoulli's equation or thermodynamic laws can be derived.

In order to find the variation of temperature along a streamline with velocity changes, write Bernoulli's equation for free air values on the left side and the values at any other point on the right, represented by subscript x:

$$\frac{V^2}{2} + \frac{\gamma}{\gamma - 1} \frac{P}{\rho} = \frac{V_x^2}{2} + \frac{\gamma}{\gamma - 1} \frac{P_x}{\rho_x} \quad (7:1)$$

Substituting $\rho = \rho_0 (P/P_0) (T_0/T)$ and $\rho_x = \rho_0 (P_x/P_0) (T_0/T_x)$ and solving for the temperature at point x:

$$T_x = T + \frac{\rho_0 T_0 (\gamma - 1)}{2 P_0 \gamma} (V^2 - V_x^2) \quad (7:2)$$

Thus the temperature at point x differs from the free air temperature by the effect of the velocity change expressed in the last term of equation 7:2. As the velocity at point x is greater or less than the free air value, then the corresponding local air temperature will fall below or rise above the free air temperature. Thus if a pickup capable of measuring the local, or static, temperature were used, it would be subject to the same sort of troublesome position error encountered at the static pressure orifices of the airspeed head. If, however, the pickup were designed to record the stopped air, or total, temperature, it would have no location error, similarly with the total head pressure at the airspeed head. It becomes apparent that the logical approach to the problem is to measure the total temperature and then by calculation eliminate the temperature rise due to adiabatic compression. This temperature rise for

$V_x = 0$ from the last term of equation 7:2 in terms of degrees centigrade and free air velocity in mph is:

$$\Delta t_t = \left(\frac{V}{100.3}\right)^2 \quad (7:3)$$

This expression is not useful in correcting flight test values because the true air velocity cannot be accurately determined until the true free air temperature is known. However, this simple relation is very convenient in evaluating mentally the magnitude of this temperature rise, that is, at 400 mph the total adiabatic temperature rise is 16°C.

This total temperature rise can be derived in terms of Mach number.

$$\sigma = \frac{\rho}{\rho_0} = \frac{PT_0}{P_0 T} \quad (7:4)$$

and the speed of sound may be determined by

$$V_c = \sqrt{\frac{\gamma P}{\rho}} \text{ or, in engineering units,}$$

$$V_c = 44.85 \sqrt{T} \quad (7:5)$$

where T is free air temperature in degrees Kelvin (°C + 273) and V_c is in mph. From these equations, the constants which determine the sea level value of the velocity of sound in equation 7:2 may be expressed

$$\frac{\rho_0}{\gamma P_0} = \frac{T}{T_0 V_c^2} \quad (7:6)$$

When this substitution is made, the simplified result becomes

$$\Delta t_t = .2 \, TM^2 \quad (7:7)$$

Unfortunately, most temperature pickups in use do not record this full adiabatic temperature rise, but are affected by some relatively constant proportion, K, of it:

$$\Delta t_m = .2 \, KTM^2 \quad (7:8)$$

From this equation the solution for the actual free air temperature in terms of the temperature measured by a specific pickup and the Mach number at which the measurement was taken is:

$$T = \frac{T_m}{(1 + .2 \, KM^2)} \quad (7:9)$$

By testing, the value of K, the recovery factor, for any given pickup may be determined and a direct solution for true airspeed becomes possible. Mach number was determined from the airspeed and the altimeter readings. Now the true air temperature, upon which the speed of sound depends, is obtained from this equation. Then the true free airspeed is simply the product of the free air values of Mach number and the velocity of sound.

7.3 Free Air Pickup Calibration

Having located the free air pickup in a region of streamline flow removed from any possible influence of power plant or propeller and shielded from the sun, flight tests may be conducted to

goal is a well-shielded and insulated pickup having minimum lag characteristics to temperature changes and a K factor equalling 1.0. In a proper installation, this pickup would have no location, or position, error. Furthermore, the complications introduced into true airspeed and temperature reduction could be eliminated, and a very simple universal solution would result.

If the pickup value of K is constant, as is usually the case, particularly in the range of speeds obtained during speed runs, then a plot of measured temperature versus the square of Mach number will be a straight line; see equation 7:9. Then if this straight line is extrapolated to zero

TABLE 6. DETERMINATION OF RECOVERY FACTOR, K — DATA REDUCTION

V_m		131	161	190	220	250	279	299
V_{cal}		133	164	194	225	256	286	307
H_{p_m}		15,135	15,115	15,075	15,035	14,985	14,965	14,895
H_p		15,165	15,165	15,165	15,165	15,165	15,165	15,165
M^*	0	.232	.287	.338	.391	.444	.496	.530
M^2		.054	.082	.114	.153	.196	.246	.281
t_m		−21.2	−20.1	−19.0	−17.0	−16.0	−14.8	−12.4
t	−23.1	—	—	—	—	—	—	—
Δt_m		1.9	3.0	4.1	6.1	7.1	8.3	10.7
T	250	—	—	—	—	—	—	—
$.2 TM^2$		2.7	4.1	5.7	7.65	9.8	12.3	14.0
K		.70	.73	.72	.78	.72	.68	.76

* From Figure 8:1

calibrate the pickup. Temperature readings at constant altitude and varying airspeeds are taken. It is assumed that the free air temperature in the testing zone is constant, so the airplane should be flown within a certain restricted locality. Any possible attitude in which the sun's rays may conceivably affect the pickup should be avoided. Also, heat from the sun may be radiating from

Mach number, where the measured and free air temperatures are equal, the free air temperature is determined. The actual temperature rises for each test point are then known and compared with the adiabatic temperature rise for stopped airflow. In order to obtain the maximum possible Mach number spread for the test points, the tests should be run at a high altitude and at a low altitude, but not less than a few thousand feet from the ground.

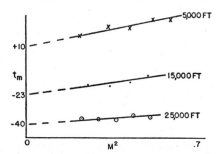

Fig. 7:7. Plot of measured temperature versus Mach number squared for several altitudes

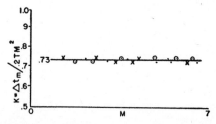

Fig. 7:8. Recovery factor test results plotted against Mach number

clouds, or from varying types of terrain if in too close proximity to the ground. Moisture or ice condensing or evaporating on the pickup could destroy the results.

It may be emphasized here that the ultimate

The operations of calibrating the free air temperature pickup are illustrated in Figures 7:7 and 7:8 and by the sample calculations given in Table 6.

Data required: t_r, V_r, H_{p_r}.

Note that the pilot has been given different altitudes at which to fly the various speeds according to the position error (Chapter 5) in order that the tests points will be obtained at a constant pressure altitude level.

Typical K values for different pickups are noted in Figures 7:1-7:6.

Because the data obtained may be scattered, it is well to make a considerable number of test runs in order to arrive at a good average value. After finishing a series of runs, the first two runs or so should be repeated to insure the validity of the data, that is, that the results can be duplicated and that the temperature conditions have not changed.

7.4 Graphical Solution

Having evaluated K, equation 7:9 is used in the reduction of data to free air temperature. A graphical solution of this expression is presented in Figures 8:2a and 8:2b. The parameter $M \sqrt{K}$ is used so that the curve may be used for any pickup. Obviously, the curve values represent the theoretical case of full adiabatic temperature rise for $K = 1.0$. Table 7 illustrates the use of Figures 8:2a and 8:2b. Velocity of sound is included in these figures for convenience in computing true airspeed.

TABLE 7. FREE AIR TEMPERATURE
DETERMINATION — DATA REDUCTION

V_{cal}	250	250	250	250
H_p	30,000	30,000	30,000	sea level
t_m	−42.3	−38.5	−34.7	16.1
M^*	.586	.586	.586	.328
K for pickup	.5	.75	1.0	1.0
$M \sqrt{K}$	.415	.507	.586	.328
t^{**}	−50	−50	−50	10
(Δt_m)	(7.7)	(11.5)	(15.3)	(6.1)

* From Figure 8:1
** From Figure 8:2

CHAPTER 8

TRUE AIRSPEED DATA REDUCTION

8.1 Discussion

The foregoing chapters have indicated the theory of true airspeed measurement from the readings in flight of the airspeed indicator, altimeter, and temperature indicator. The graphical solutions for the complicated operations are given in this chapter in Figures 8:1 and 8:2.

In addition, it is usually desired to know the density ratio and/or density altitude at which

TABLE 8. TRUE AIRSPEED DETERMINATION — DATA REDUCTION

V_m	280 mph	V_r — lab. inst. cal. error.*
ΔV_{pe}	−7 mph	From airspeed position error curve such as Figure 5:3.
V_{cal}	287 mph	$V_m - \Delta V_{pe}$.
H_{P_m}	25,500 ft	H_{P_r} — lab. inst. cal. error.
ΔH_p	−330 ft	From altimeter position error curve such as Figure 5:3.
H_p	25,830 ft	$H_{P_m} - \Delta H_p$.
t_m	−25°C	t_r — lab. inst. cal. error.
M	.612	From Figure 8:1c for V_{cal} and H_p.
K	.75	Free air temperature pickup calibration, Figure 7:4.
$M \sqrt{K}$	.530	
t	−38°C	From Fig. 8:2a for t_m and $M \sqrt{K}$.
V_c	687 mph	From Figure 8:2a for t.
V	421 mph	$V = MV_c$.
σ	.438	From Figure 8:3c for t and H_p.
H_D	25,650 ft	From Figure 8:3c for σ.

*Laboratory instrument calibration error, so abbreviated in the data reduction tables.

the data were obtained, which is read from Figure 8:3. (See reference 1.) Entering the figure with true free air temperature and true pressure altitude, the density ratio, σ, is read directly.

Standard N.A.C.A. atmospheric conditions are represented by the standard line. Since, by definition, density altitude is the absolute altitude in a standard atmosphere at which a given density is to be found, interpolate the density altitude on the standard line for the density ratio desired.

Based upon the theory outlined in the previous chapters, a circular true airspeed computer can be designed with sufficient accuracy for flight test data reduction. From the values of calibration airspeed, true pressure altitude, and measured air temperature, the values of Mach number, free air temperature, true airspeed, density ratio, and density altitude may be evaluated instantly and accurately. Labor saving, accuracy, ease of checking, and reverse calculations are its chief merits.

8.2 Method

The data required are:

(a) Observed airspeed, V_r.

(b) Observed pressure altitude, H_{p_r}.

(c) Observed free air temperature, t_r.

(d) Instrument calibration curves.

(e) Airspeed and altimeter position error calibration for the type of airspeed head installation used (see Figure 5:3).

(f) Free air temperature pickup calibration for the type of pickup used (see Section 7.3).

Table 8 illustrates the true airspeed determination for a typical set of data from a wing boom type airspeed head installation and an electrical resistance free air pickup.

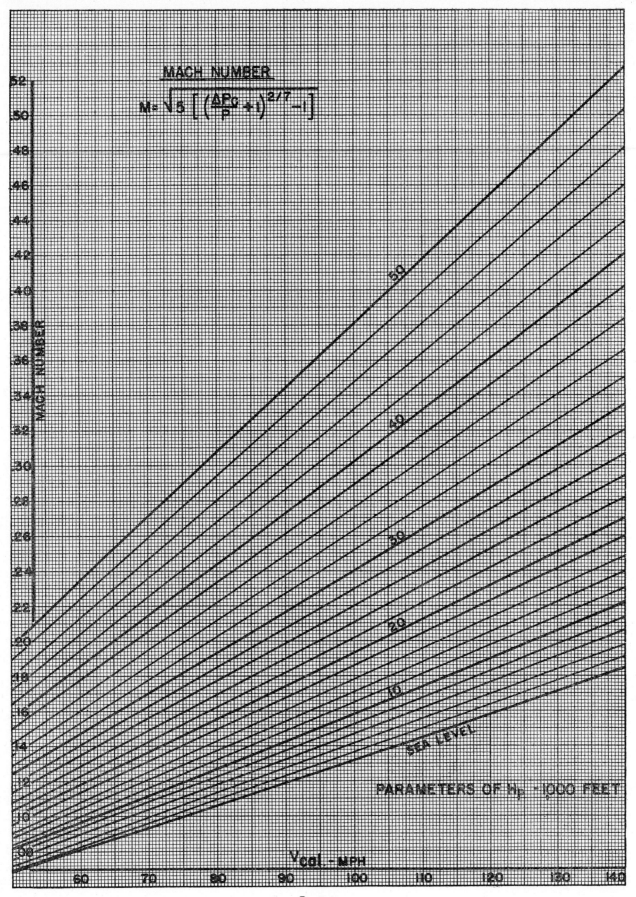

Fig. 8:1a

33

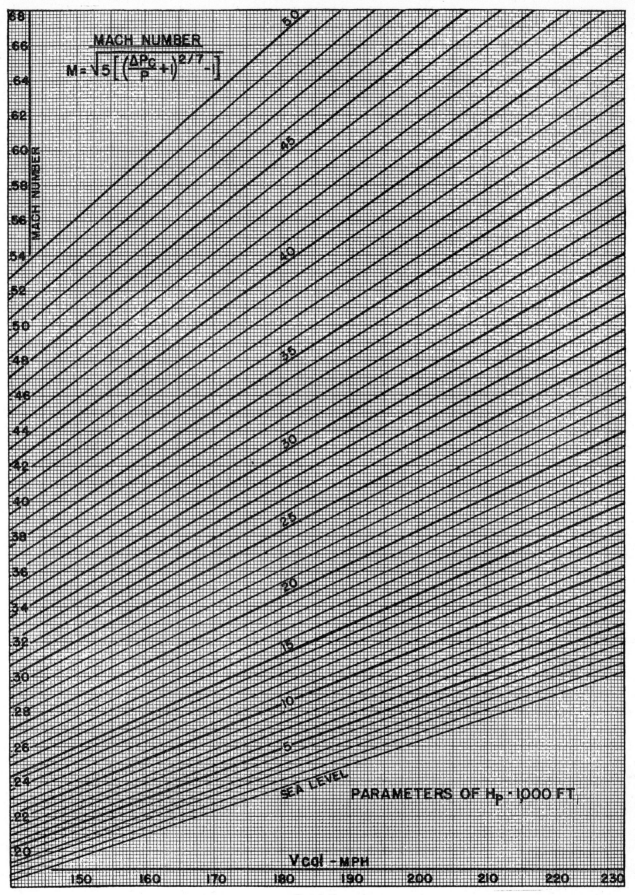

MACH NUMBER

$$M = \sqrt{5\left[\left(\frac{\Delta P_G}{P}+1\right)^{2/7}-1\right]}$$

MACH NUMBER

PARAMETERS OF $H_P \cdot 1000$ FT

SEA LEVEL

V_{cal} - MPH

Fig. 8:1b

34

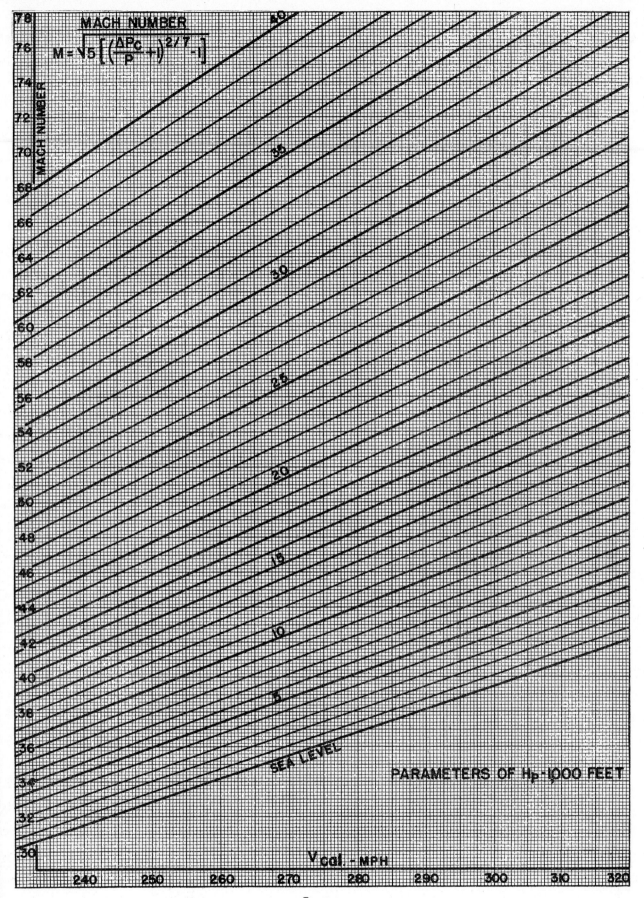

$$M = \sqrt{5\left[\left(\frac{\Delta P_C}{P}+1\right)^{2/7}-1\right]}$$

MACH NUMBER

MACH NUMBER

SEA LEVEL

PARAMETERS OF Hp - 1,000 FEET

V cal. - MPH

Fig. 8:1c

35

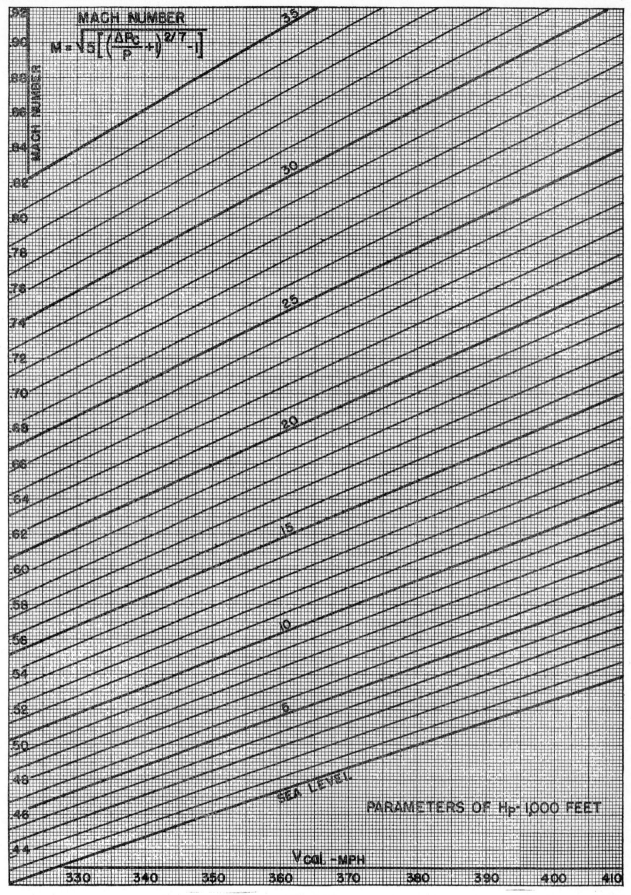

Fig. 8:1d

36

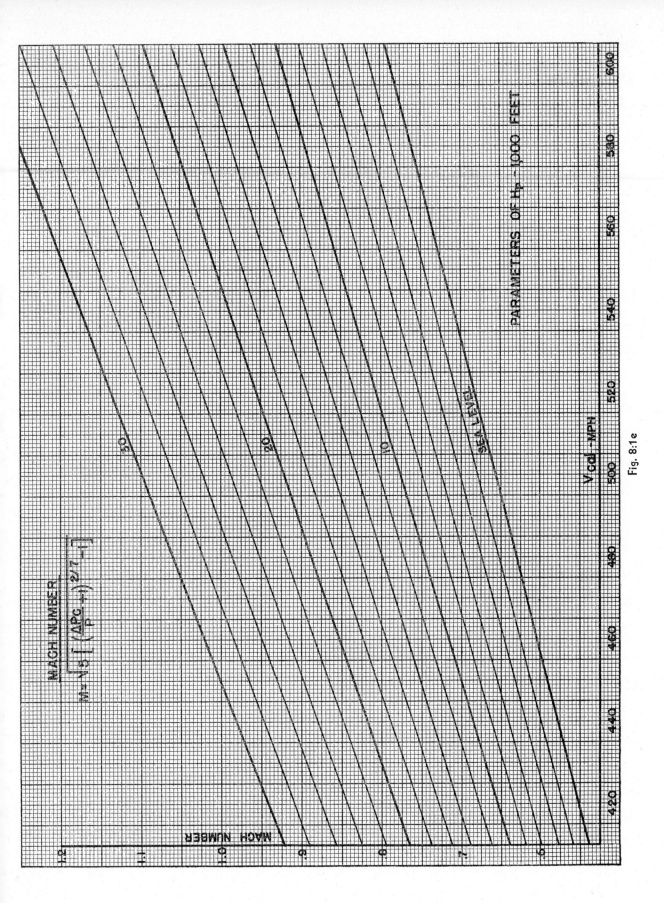

MACH NUMBER

$$M = \sqrt{5\left[\left(\frac{\Delta P_G}{P} + 1\right)^{2/7} - 1\right]}$$

Fig. 8:1e

PARAMETERS OF H_P – 1,000 FEET

V_{cal} – MPH

SEA LEVEL

MACH NUMBER

37

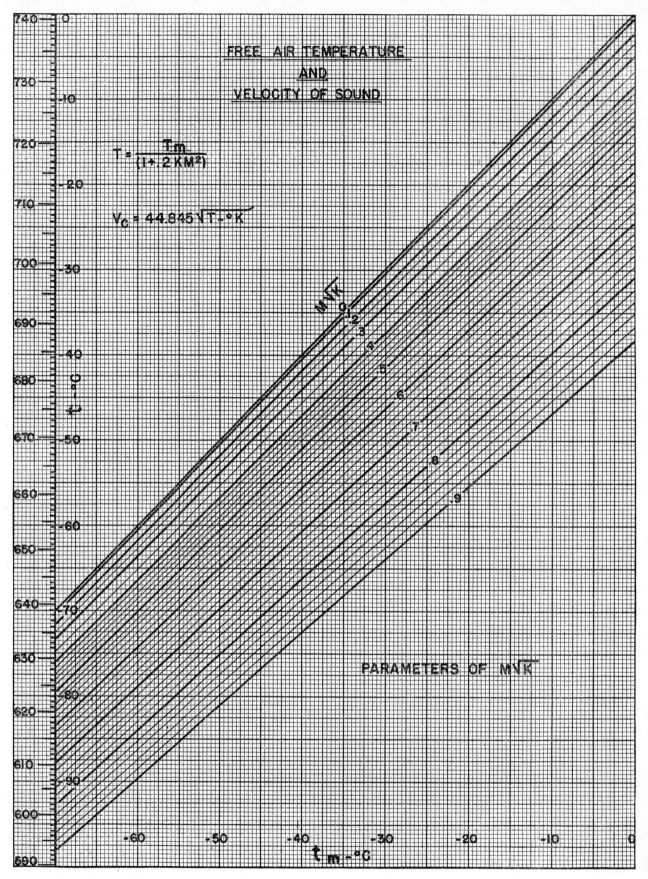

FREE AIR TEMPERATURE
AND
VELOCITY OF SOUND

$$T = \frac{T_m}{(1 + .2 \, KM^2)}$$

$$V_c = 44.845 \sqrt{T \cdot {}^\circ K}$$

$M \sqrt{K}$

PARAMETERS OF $M \sqrt{K}$

t_m - °C

Fig. 8:2a

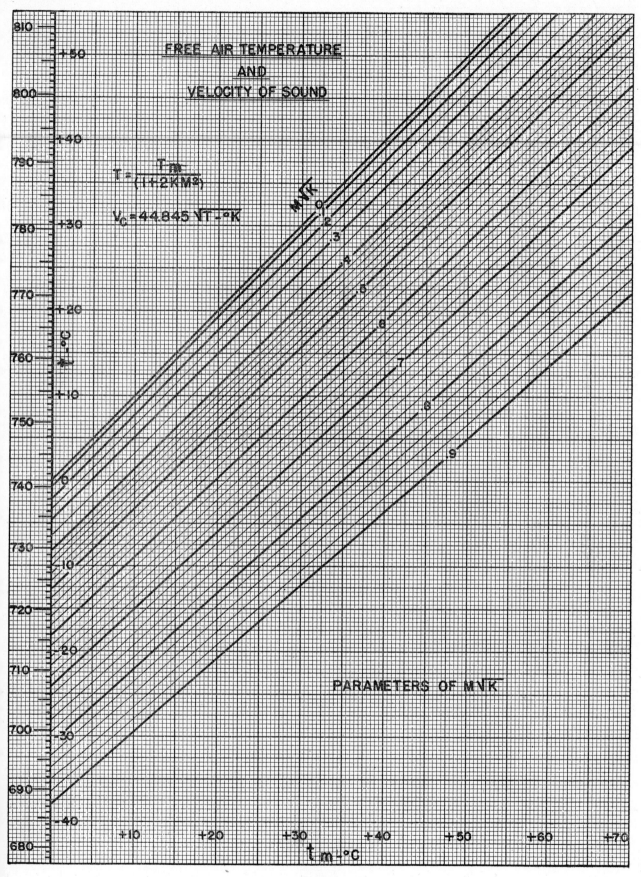

FREE AIR TEMPERATURE
AND
VELOCITY OF SOUND

$$T = \frac{T_m}{(1 + 2KM^2)}$$

$$V_C = 44.845 \sqrt{T} \cdot °K$$

PARAMETERS OF $M\sqrt{K}$

$t_m - °C$

Fig. 8:2b

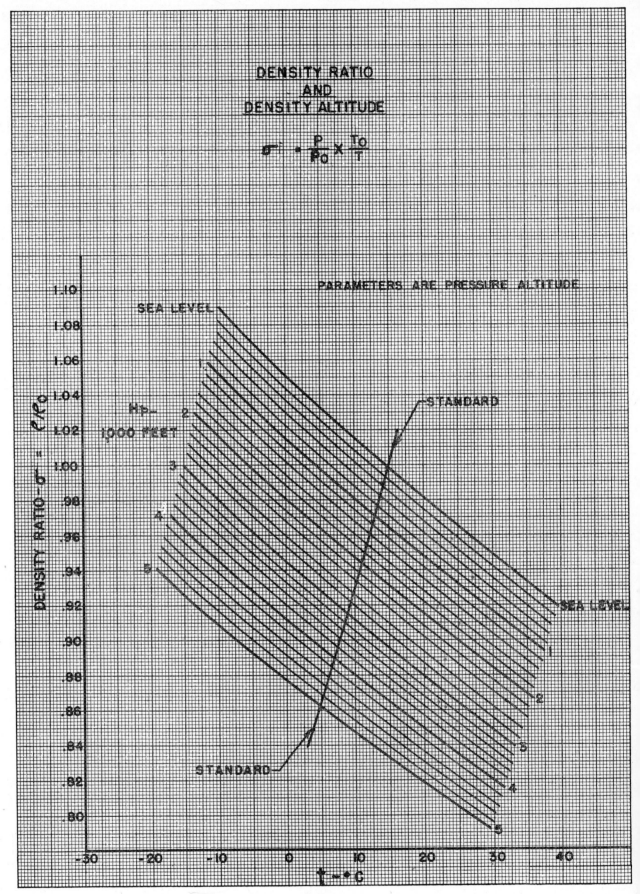

Fig. 8:3a

40

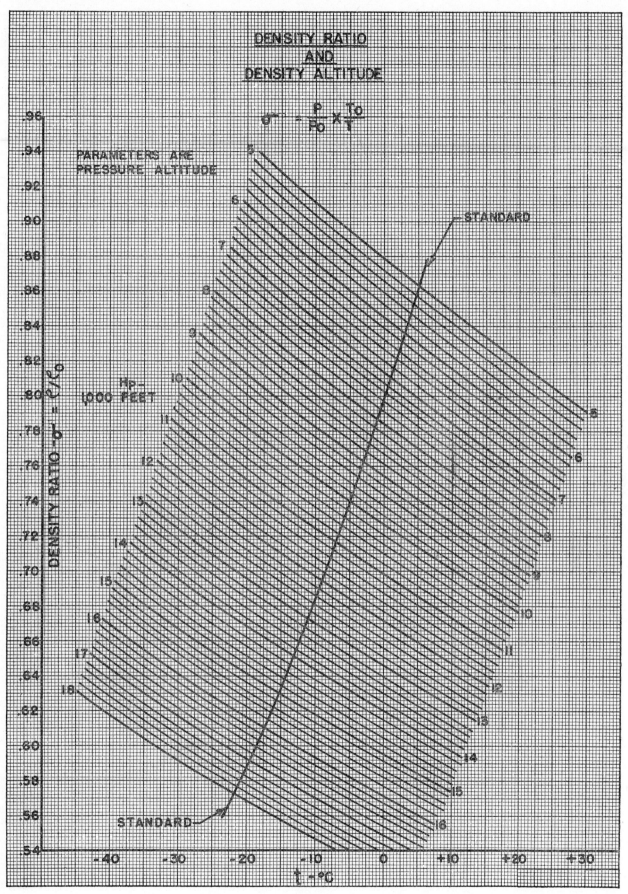

Fig. 8:3b

41

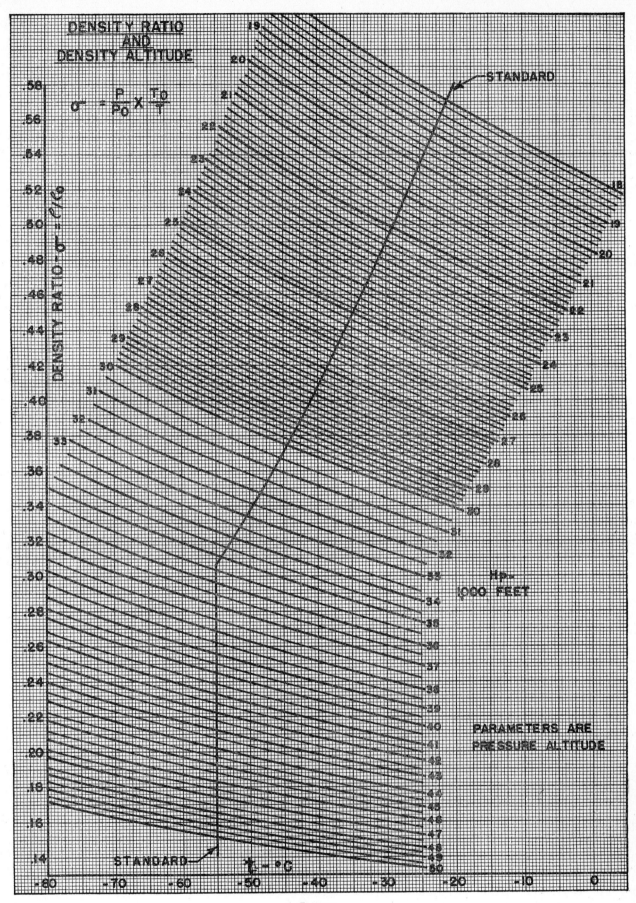

Fig. 8:3c

42

CHAPTER 9

STALLING SPEED

9.1 Discussion

Stalling speeds from flight test must be reduced to the maximum lift coefficient, $C_{L\max}$, which is the characteristic of the airplane, that is, stalling speed will vary with gross weight while $C_{L\max}$ is independent of it.

Following is a list of variables which may affect stalling speeds and $C_{L\max}$:

(a) Airplane configuration: landing flaps, cowl flaps, cabins, and other variable parts.

(b) Propeller position or rpm.

(c) Reynolds number: $f(V, H_p, t)$.

(d) Rate of change of angle of attack: $d\alpha/dt$.

(e) Vibration.

(f) Wing surface: weathering, service wear, dirt, and other maintenance items.

(g) Dynamic unbalance of airspeed system.

(h) Change in wing rigging with service and time.

(i) Center of gravity location.

A study of these variables reveals the careful attention and observation as well as test procedure required in order to insure accurate results. Complete information on the actual configuration of the airplane at the time of the individual tests, and notes on the characteristics of the stalls and any irregularities in stalling technique, should be recorded. Stalls should be made by reducing speed as slowly and uniformly as possible to avoid unsymmetrical wing stalling and exaggerated values of $C_{L\max}$ attainable by excessive rate of change of attitude, $d\alpha/dt$. Dynamic unbalance is mentioned because the instrumentation affecting the airspeed system is often changed during flight testing. The Reynolds number effect is usually small; increasing Reynolds numbers will increase $C_{L\max}$. Center of gravity location affects the tail load and, in turn, the airplane maximum lift coefficient.

In general, under the most carefully controlled identical test conditions, a maximum dispersion in $C_{L\max}$ of about 3 per cent (1.5 per cent in speed) may be expected.

Stalling speeds are measured most successfully by means of the trailing bomb, Figure 5:5. Without the trailing bomb, recourse must be had to the extrapolated airspeed position error curve, which must be available for various landing flap positions, and, unless available for glide condition, the dynamic unbalance error will be unknown. If the true position error curve is available, the true stalling speeds may be obtained from the airplane airspeed indicator readings.

9.2 Data Reduction

At least four stalling speeds must be obtained for each condition tested. Reduce these to true equivalent airspeeds (obtained directly from balanced trailing bomb), and find the average value. Note by reference to Figure 4:2 that the difference between V_{cal} and $V\sqrt{\sigma}$ is negligible for stalling speeds.

In order to calculate $C_{L\max}$, the gross weight at the time of stall must be known, so the curve of gross weight during flight versus time is necessary. If a fuel flowmeter is installed, it should be read at enough intervals to supply the data required for such a curve. When better data are not available, such a curve is drawn, assuming that the rate of fuel consumption during climb and level flight is twice that during glide. Knowing the total fuel consumed during flight and the times at which climbs and glides were begun and ended, calculations are made as follows:

$$\text{Let} \qquad t = \text{flight time (in minutes)},$$
$$t_g = \text{glide and stall time (in minutes)},$$
$$(\text{lb/min})_g = \text{fuel consumption during } t_g,$$
$$2(\text{lb/min})_g = \text{fuel consumption during } (t - t_g) \qquad (9{:}1)$$

Total lb = weight of fuel consumed during flight

Then

$$(\text{lb}/\text{min})_g = \frac{\text{total lb}}{(2t - t_g)} \qquad (9:2)$$

Using equations 9:2 and 9:1, a typical gross weight-time curve, Figure 9:1, is calculated.

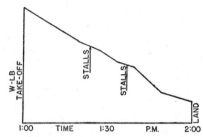

Fig. 9:1. Variation of gross weight during flight

Having tabulated the average value of $V\sqrt{\sigma}$ and the actual gross weight for each set of stalls tested, $C_{L\text{max}}$ is calculated by:

$$C_{L\text{max}} = \frac{391\,W}{S(V\sqrt{\sigma})^2} \qquad (9:3)$$

The final desired curve of the results is indicated in Figure 9:2.

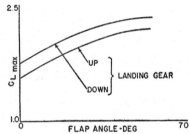

Fig. 9:2. Variation of maximum lift coefficient with flap angle

Any other pertinent data (see Section 9:1), should be recorded with the final curve. Stalling speed at any desired gross weight and configuration is then calculated from these maximum lift coefficients by:

$$V_0 = V\sqrt{\sigma} = \sqrt{\frac{391\,W}{S C_{L\text{max}}}} \qquad (9:4)$$

Assuming the $C_{L\text{max}}$ of the wing alone is a fixed characteristic, the change in airplane $C_{L\text{max}}$ caused by a change in center of gravity (CG) position, which in turn causes a change in the proportion of total gross weight carried by the wing and tail each, may easily be calculated. Equating wing lift and gross weight moments about the tail force location (elevator hinge line) will give the useful equation 9:5. The standard tail length to wing aerodynamic chord ratio may be used with negligible error. As expressed, the equation is useful for simple calculations of the effect of large center of gravity variations, and if $\Delta C_{L\text{max}}$ is sufficiently great, the $C_{L\text{max}}$ curves should be drawn for a range of center of gravity locations.

$$(C_{L\text{max}})_2 = (C_{L\text{max}})_1$$
$$+ \left(\frac{CG_2 - CG_1}{l_1/\text{MAC} - CG_1}\right)(C_{L\text{max}})_1 \quad (9:5)$$

9.3 Data Required

Weight at take-off and landing.
Center of gravity position.
Sufficient data to determine history of gross weight throughout the flight.

Time.
Flap angle.   } For each set of stalls.
Other configuration.

Airplane V_r.   } For each stall.
Bomb V_r.

Pressure altitude, rpm, temperature: desirable data.

Notes: Any pertinent notes on technique, configuration, airplane action, and stall characteristics, including altitude loss in recovery, should be recorded.

Some judgment and experience is necessary in determining the correct airspeed reading at which the actual and full stall occurs. Since the airspeed reading is changing and unsteady, very close concentration is necessary in order to read the speed at the instant of stalling.

A complete check of the airspeed line system for leaks must be made before and after each flight.

CHAPTER 10

ENGINE AND POWER CHARACTERISTICS

10.1 Theory of Power Curves

There is no substitute for a torquemeter for determining accurately the brake horsepower output of an engine, in which case $(BHP)_Q = K \times$ (torquemeter pressure gauge reading) $\times$ RPM. Unfortunately, torquemeters are unavailable for some engines. In such a case, the engine manufacturer's power charts must be used to determine the brake horsepower, and since power plays a vitally important role in data reduction, a brief discussion of engine theory and use of power charts is essential.

A typical power chart is shown in Figure 10:1.

through a given negative horsepower (motoring power required to drive the engine) at zero manifold pressure.

(b) Curves of sea level brake horsepower versus manifold pressure for constant rpm are almost always straight lines. The manifold pressures and powers increase as the throttle is opened, and the upper limit is reached, of course, at full throttle.

(c) Variation of brake horsepower with atmospheric density, on the altitude calibration part of the chart, for constant rpm's and full throttle, is a straight line, and the brake horsepower be-

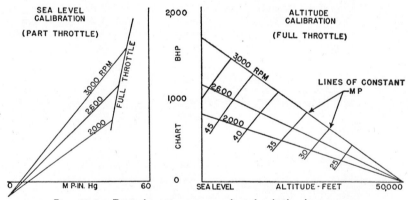

Fig. 10:1. Typical engine power chart for brake horsepower determination

For naturally aspirated or gear-driven supercharged engines, the following observations have been found to apply to four-cycle internal combustion aircraft engines. These facts make it possible to draw complete calibration curves from a comparatively small amount of engine test data, although thorough tests should be made in order to construct a completely reliable power chart. These fundamentals are included here as they are often used.

(a) Engine friction horsepower is practically independent of rpm for closed throttle. This phenomenon accounts for the fact that all rpm lines in the sea level calibration curve pass

comes zero in the neighborhood of 55,000 ft for all such engines. It is for this reason that the standard altitude scale in feet on these power charts is a nonlinear scale, as it is really a linear density scale. Because of the limited number of altitude pressure chambers, complete altitude calibration curves from engine test data are not always available.

(d) Lines of constant manifold pressure are superimposed on the altitude calibration curves from test data. Full throttle manifold pressures for any given rpm also will plot very nearly as straight lines when plotted against density.

(e) In Figure 10:2 is a plot of the power factor

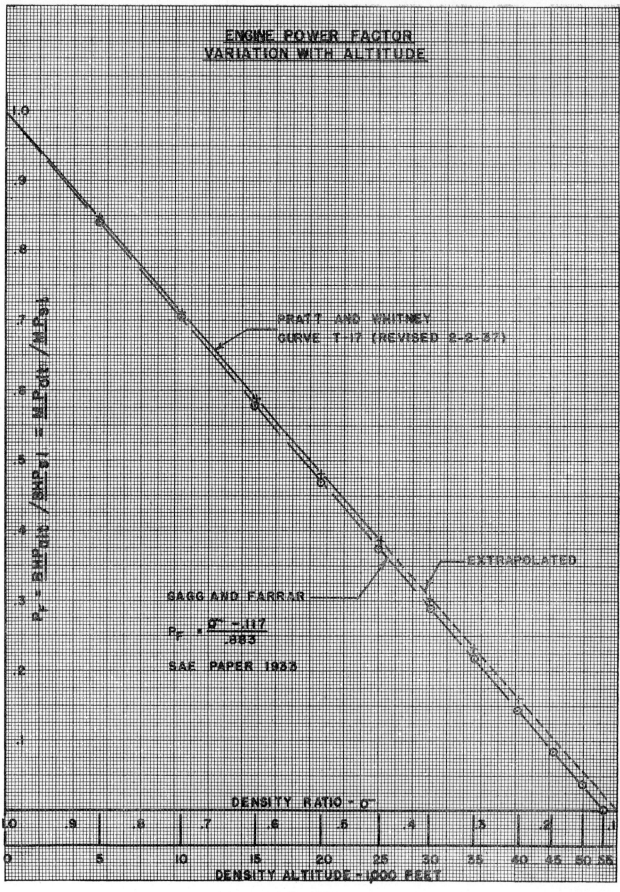

ENGINE POWER FACTOR
VARIATION WITH ALTITUDE

PRATT AND WHITNEY
CURVE T-17 (REVISED 2-2-37)

EXTRAPOLATED

GAGG AND FARRAR

$$P_F = \frac{\sigma - .117}{.883}$$

SAE PAPER 1933

$P_F = \frac{BHP_0'}{BHP_0} = \frac{M.P.0'}{M.P.0}$

DENSITY RATIO - σ

DENSITY ALTITUDE - 1000 FEET

Fig. 10:2

($P_f =$ BHP$_{alt}$/BHP$_{sl}$) against density ratio. This factor also may be used for manifold pressures in lieu of better information. Thus, it is seen, for instance, that for *full throttle* and a *constant* rpm both the brake horsepower and the manifold pressure at 20,000 ft standard altitude will be 47 per cent of their respective full throttle sea level values. In the case of two-speed superchargers these facts are applicable to each blower ratio; in other words, each blower ratio will produce performance equivalent to different engines.

These facts become very useful in extending the range of data on any given power chart.

10.2 Brake Horsepower Determination from Power Curves

Having the sea level part throttle and altitude full throttle engine curves, the next step is to determine any part throttle power at altitude. This process is illustrated in Figure 10:3.

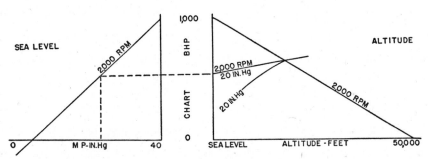

Fig. 10:3.   Illustration of the use of an engine power chart

The brake horsepower at a given rpm, manifold pressure, and altitude is desired for values obtained by part throttle operation.

(a) Determine the brake horsepower for the given 2,000 rpm and 20 in. Hg manifold pressure from the sea level chart and spot this power at sea level on the altitude chart.

(b) On the altitude chart, spot the intersection of the 2,000 rpm and 20 in. Hg manifold pressure lines.

(c) Connect these two points by a straight line. This line then represents the brake horsepower variation with altitude for constant 2,000 rpm and 20 in. Hg manifold pressure. The straight line variation in the plot has been observed to be the true variation as verified by test. This increase in power with altitude is the net result of the effect of reduced exhaust back pressure, lower carburetor air temperature, and less throttling loss, all tending to increase the brake horsepower output,

and the increasing supercharger power required tending to reduce the brake horsepower output.

(d) It then remains simply to read the brake horsepower from this straight line for the altitude desired, which will be referred to as the chart power, BHP$_{ch}$.

In the preceding discussion, all of the above curves are based upon standard atmospheric conditions, that is, standard atmospheric temperature and pressure at the carburetor inlet and engine exhaust. Since these conditions are never standard, a correction must be applied to the chart power, BHP$_{ch}$. The procedure for determining the actual output — brake horsepower — of the engine will be as follows:

Data required: pressure altitude, H_p; rpm; manifold pressure, MP; and carburetor air temperature, t_c.

First find the chart power, BHP$_{ch}$, from the power charts based on pressure altitude, rpm, and manifold pressure, exactly as has been outlined. It is standard practice to use the airplane pressure altitude, disregarding the fact that both the exhaust back pressure and carburetor entrance pressure may be different from the airplane pressure altitude and from each other. Correct this chart power to the true or actual power by multiplying by the square root of the ratio of the standard absolute carburetor air temperature (that is standard absolute free air temperature) to the actual absolute carburetor air temperature.

$$\text{BHP} = \text{BHP}_{ch}\left(\frac{t_s + 273}{t_c + 273}\right)^{.5} = \text{BHP}_{ch}\left(\frac{T_s}{T_c}\right)^{.5}$$
$$(10:1)$$

This carburetor air temperature correction, at constant manifold pressure, has been in use for many years and is well substantiated. It is always to be used in determining actual powers from chart powers, and is not to be confused with determination of what an actual power would have been had the atmospheric conditions been standard as handled in Chapter 11.

The curves shown in Figure 10:3 for supercharged engines are usually cut off at some constant rated power by the engine manufacturer simply because such engines are structurally incapable of operating at full throttle outputs at low altitudes. Decision of the power limitation for continuous operation or specified limited time rests on the highest mean effective pressure within the cylinders and the highest rpm the engine will safely withstand. Thus, the brake mean effective pressure (BMEP) is a useful measure of the severity of engine operation for a given rpm, and must be considered in rated power and also high cruising power operation, to avoid overstressing the engine.

$$BMEP = \frac{792,000 \ (BHP)}{(RPM)d} = lb/in.^2 \quad (10:2)$$

10.3 Types of Power Curves

For engines having superchargers driven by exhaust turbos, the supercharger rpm becomes independent of engine rpm, and the basic theory just stated is no longer applicable. Constant critical turbo speed or manifold inlet temperatures may impose the critical limitation to allowable engine operation rather than manifold pressure. The complicated problems involving turbos are left to specialized sources of which references 8 and 9 are mentioned.

A two-stage, two-speed, gear-driven supercharged engine exhibits the same characteristics as have been described when each supercharger gear ratio configuration is considered to represent an entirely different engine. Since the full supercharging at sea level would produce full throttle engine powers much greater than the engine could possibly withstand structurally, it is impossible to make use of the higher blower gear ratios at low altitudes. Conversely, since the engine must be throttled at low altitude, it is foolishly inefficient to tolerate this high degree of supercharging to be nullified by throttling. One of the natural developments has been to gear the auxiliary blower to select zero, a low-, or a high-gear ratio. The result is shown in Figure 10:4 where the dotted lines represent the three "individual" engine characteristics at constant rpm and the solid line the engine manufacturer's rating, approximately constant indicated horsepower.

Sea level calibrations at the high blower ratios are usually not available. For a given manifold

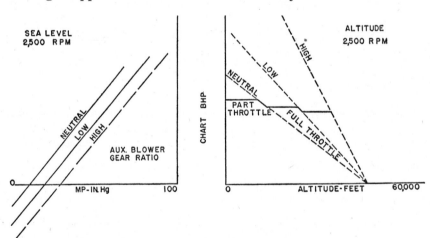

Fig. 10:4. Typical power chart at maximum engine rpm for a variable-speed, gear-driven, supercharged engine

power may be maintained to a higher critical altitude, a design criterion, than with gear-driven superchargers, and neither the altitude of zero brake horsepower output nor the full throttle brake horsepower variation with altitude as just mentioned are applicable.

Also, for turbo supercharged power plants, pressure, the high blower speeds will give high pressures with correspondingly high temperatures. Consequently, throttling is necessary to reduce the manifold pressure to the desired value. In doing this, there is no temperature drop, so the manifold mixture temperatures rise to the point where detonation is encountered at relatively low

manifold pressures and powers. For the same
manifold pressure, the indicated horsepower remains constant, but at the higher blower ratios
more power is lost to driving the auxiliary supercharger, with a consequent reduction in brake
horsepower available to drive the propeller.
Obviously the high compression ratios at an
altitude where both the atmospheric pressure and
temperature are low will pay large dividends.

The turbo supercharger principle is to maintain
constant brake horsepower with altitude and
avoid the various compromises apparent in the
previous paragraph. Since the turbo uses energy
from the exhaust to drive a supercharger supply-
ing the engine intake manifold, it can be seen
that sea level pressure conditions can be approximated at the engine intake and exhaust even at
increasing altitudes up to critical, that is, that
altitude at which the capacity of the turbo to
meet these conditions is reached. Consequently,
constant sea level brake horsepower may be maintained to relatively high altitudes.

A basic engine is one machine and an exhaust
gas turbine is another machine with its specific
characteristics. Infinite combinations of the two
are possible, but the two components and their
characteristics must be combined and matched
properly, the result being a third machine of
characteristics unique unto itself, hence a much
more complicated power plant in the final analysis.

A third type of power plant employs a variable-
speed, hydraulically-coupled, auxiliary supercharger in an attempt to overcome the disadvantages of the variable " selected " gear ratios as
illustrated and yet to avoid the complications of
the turbo installation. In this type, variable
slippage between the driving and driven shafts to
the auxiliary blower is obtained by varying the
quantity of oil in the " coupling " mechanism.
This varying oil level is then accomplished automatically by a control receiving as its stimulus
atmospheric pressure, since the amount of supercharging desired is a function of altitude only.

The principle of operation of an engine with a
variable-speed, hydraulically-coupled, auxiliary
supercharger can best be explained with the aid
of the sketch of the altitude power curve, Figure
10:5. Curve AD represents the basic engine with
its " fixed " gear-driven main stage blower,
engine (a). Curve JD represents the same engine

with an auxiliary blower fully coupled, that is, no
slip in the coupling and consequently the gear
ratio chosen for this condition, as engine (b).
If engine (b) were rated at constant 60 in. Hg
manifold pressure, its part throttle powers would
be represented by curve BE. Note that in this
discussion the engine manufacturer has limited
power output by specifying a limiting manifold
pressure, while in Figure 10:4 the engine manufacturer limited part throttle operation by specifying a constant brake horsepower. Consider
engine (c) as an engine similar to the previously
discussed two-stage, two-speed engine, that is, the
auxiliary blower may be in neutral or in the
" fixed " gear ratio by choice. Then engine (c)
would obviously take advantage of the high output at lower altitudes by operating with the
auxiliary blower in neutral between A and K and

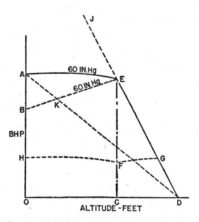

Fig. 10:5.   Engine altitude power variation for a variable-speed,
hydraulically-coupled supercharger

then throw in the auxiliary blower from point K
on to full throttle point E, and thence on up in
altitude to point D. Engine (c) is an improvement
over engine (b) by the power increase in area
AKB. Its high power at A is obtained at the same
60 in. Hg manifold pressure resulting from full
throttle operation, while point B represented
throttled conditions and loss in power to run the
second supercharger.

It now is obvious that still another engine is
desirable, one that is still better than either (a),
(b), or (c). Engine (d) becomes one which takes
advantage of point A for engine (a) and point E
for engines (b) or (c), but avoids any part
throttle operation between points A and E with
attendant power lost to the auxiliary supercharger. Thus the hydraulically coupled supercharger drive comes into its own by increasing

the blower rpm with increase in altitude by the proper schedule such that 60 in. Hg manifold pressure is maintained with full throttle. This most efficient supercharging system results in powers shown by line AE, and the power previously gone to waste to the supercharger in area AEK is now retrieved.

Note that at altitude EC, full coupling is attained, so that above this altitude the engine characteristics are the same as engines (b) or (c). Thus part throttle operation above altitude C is represented by power FG, but below this altitude the supercharger speed will be varied, based on atmospheric pressure, to maintain approximately constant power HF. Of course, at sea level, the auxiliary blower is merely idling at practically zero shaft horsepower.

The reason for limiting the manifold pressure in this case was because of detonation occurring at higher intake pressures and temperatures. Consequently, the next step was water injection to postpone detonation to much higher manifold pressures and hence powers.

The next chapter on aircraft power plants has been written by jet propulsion units, and the next phases of the internal combustion engines will be transitional between the two unique power plants.

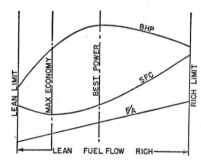

Fig. 10:6.   Variation of power, fuel consumption, and fuel-air ratio with fuel flow at constant rpm and throttle setting

10.4 Effect of Mixture on Power

The effect of fuel-air ratio, or mixture, on brake horsepower output is best illustrated by Figure 10:6. These curves are drawn for a constant rpm and a constant throttle setting, but varying rates of fuel flow through the carburetor.

In leaning the mixture, a point will be reached at which the engine will become rough, backfire,

stop running, or overheat. Too rich a mixture will cause uneven running or stoppage. *Best Power* and *Best Power Mixture* refer to those values at which the maximum brake horsepower occurs. *Economical Power* and *Maximum Economy Mixture* (or *Best Economy*) refers to those values at which the specific fuel consumption, SFC = lb/(BHP)(hr), is a minimum. Automatic carburetors are adjusted to give best power operation for the automatic rich setting and economical power operation for the automatic lean setting, adjusted slightly richer than the optimum values to allow a safe margin for variables such as manufacturing tolerances in the carburetor mechanisms. At extreme powers such as take-off power, very rich mixtures are necessary to avoid overheating, in which case the excess fuel will help cool the engine. Full Rich carburetor setting produces this judicious fuel flow. In addition, hand leaning may be employed, in which case the pilot manually leans the carburetor for desired operation.

The previous discussion reveals the importance of mixture setting in power determination. Unfortunately, all engine manufacturer's power curves are drawn for the best power condition (unless Full Rich is specified for military power), and power curves for other mixture settings are rarely available. Use must be made of the best data at hand.

Again the need for torquemeters, which determine actual power, is apparent for flight test work. Other uncontrollable variables differing from engine test stand conditions which affect the accuracy of power as determined from typical power curves are:

(a) Spark plug and general ignition system condition.

(b) Mixture distribution with particular air-scoop design.

(c) Engine cylinder temperatures and temperature distribution.

(d) Accessory loads.

(e) Exhaust back pressure.

(f) Carburetor air ram.

(g) Carburetor air temperature.

(h) Water vapor.

(i) Fuel quality.

(j) Detonation.

(k) Engine wear.

CHAPTER 11

CRITICAL ALTITUDE DETERMINATION

11.1 Purpose and Definition of Critical Altitude

The engine manufacturer's curves referred to in the preceding chapter correspond to engine performance at any standard altitude in which the engine is considered to be stationary. As installed in the airplane, the carburetor entrance air is obtained from a forward facing scoop in order to obtain ram existing by virtue of the airplane's speed. This results in obtaining a greater air pressure at the carburetor than exists in the atmosphere at the flight altitude, and, in effect, provides a slight supercharging effect. This beneficial effect depends upon carburetor scoop design, location, and airplane speed and, consequently, must be determined by flight testing any particular installation.

As a result of this ram effect, full throttle powers shown by the engine manufacturer's curve may be obtained at higher altitudes than those shown. Thus, it becomes very important to determine the airplane-engine-propeller critical altitude for any given power rating, as the maximum level flight speed will occur at the highest altitude at which this power may be obtained.

Some difficulty is introduced by virtue of the fact that the airplane is affected only by the atmospheric density, while the engine definitely distinguishes between the particular temperature and pressure which determine that density. This chapter is concerned specifically with the engine operation, while the resultant airplane operation is handled in the following chapters.

In the past, critical altitudes have sometimes been based upon a manifold pressure rating, but, as previously emphasized, the important engine rating criterion is the brake mean effective pressure developed, which depends only on brake horsepower and rpm. Therefore, critical altitude will be based on power, defined as follows:

Critical altitude is the highest altitude at which the engine manufacturer's rated power at rated rpm may be obtained in a given airplane installation in a standard atmosphere at a particular flight condition. Critical altitude in level flight is considered here, but should also be determined for climb at best climbing airspeed in a similar manner.

11.2 Power Correction Method

The airplane is flown at *full throttle* and rated rpm in level flight until equilibrium conditions are reached at each of several different altitudes. At each pressure altitude the actual powers as determined from a torquemeter or by use of power charts, as given in the preceding chapter, are corrected to what they would have been had the atmospheric temperature been standard. These standard powers are then plotted against the standard altitudes (which after the temperature correction are the same as the pressure altitudes), and critical altitude is read from this curve as that altitude where rated power obtains.

In order to correct the actual full throttle power to a full throttle power on a standard day by the effect of temperature change, a simple method of correction for practical use must be derived.

Carburetor entrance air temperature has a two-fold effect on full throttle power: *first*, it affects the density of the air entering the carburetor air scoop; this effect has already been given by equation 10:1 and used in section 10.2 in determining the actual horsepower developed in flight. Actually the carburetor air temperature on a standard day will be hotter than the atmosphere because of the adiabatic heat rise from the ram effect and other unavoidable causes, expressed as T_{cs}. Solving for the standard brake horsepower at standard carburetor air temperature from the actual power already determined for the actual carburetor air temperature, this *first* temperature effect is:

$$BHP_{s_1} = BHP \left(\frac{T_c}{T_{c_s}}\right)^{.5}$$

at constant manifold pressure   (11:1)

Note that this is the effect of temperature alone on density and that the conditions specified obtain at the same manifold pressure. This correction is complete and accurate for a nonsupercharged engine and also for a supercharged engine only when the throttle is adjusted to keep the same manifold pressure. As already discussed, this correction is accepted as standard for practical purposes.

In the case of a supercharged engine at *full throttle*, which concerns us here, there is a *second* effect of temperature on power. This is brought about because the compression ratio of a centrifugal blower decreases with increasing inlet temperatures. Consequently, a change in carburetor air scoop temperature, by virtue of changing the compression ratio, will cause a change in manifold pressure, hence density of inlet charge, and thereby alter the power output.

By supercharger theory, compression ratio can be expressed in terms of inlet temperature ratio. Calculations of manifold pressure versus carburetor air temperature may then be made, and by using the specific engine power chart the effect of this manifold pressure change on power may be ascertained. The net result may be condensed to a simple relation between power and carburetor air temperature directly for this *second* temperature effect by means of the relationship:

$$(BHP_2)_{ch} = (BHP_1)_{ch} \left(\frac{T_1}{T_2}\right)^{x}$$

for constant manifold temperature   (11:2)

Evaluation of the exponent x by this method is described fully in the following section. The equation given shows how chart powers vary with the *second* temperature effect, which has been translated into terms of manifold pressure variation while the first temperature effect is not included as the chart powers are still for standard carburetor entrance temperature. Only the effect of manifold pressure change is demonstrated, but it is given in terms of the temperatures which caused it and in which we are interested.

Now that the experimental value is known, we may rewrite equation 11:2 in terms of the actual and desired standard values:

$$BHP_s = BHP_{s_1}\left(\frac{T_c}{T_{c_s}}\right)^{x}$$ (11:3)

The two-fold temperature effect from equations 11:1 and 11:3 are combined into the following where the exponent $n = x + .5$:

$$BHP_s = BHP \left(\frac{T_c}{T_{c_s}}\right)^{.5} \left(\frac{T_c}{T_{c_s}}\right)^{x} = BHP \left(\frac{T_c}{T_{c_s}}\right)^{n}$$ (11:4)

This equation is the basis of determining standard brake horsepower on a standard day from the actual brake horsepower under the test conditions for a fixed throttle condition. Determination of standard carburetor temperature is outlined in section 11.4. The exponent n is determined for the compression ratio of the supercharger staging considered, which will be a function of engine rpm at fixed blower gear ratio configurations. Having once determined n by the method in the following section, data reduction is greatly simplified.

11.3 Determination of Temperature Exponent

A detailed analysis of the temperature exponent determination is given in reference 19, from which sufficient data for use are included here.

A centrifugal supercharger merely accelerates air particles up to speeds in the range of sonic velocities by whirling them radially outward. At the periphery of the blower, the particles have a velocity approximately equal to the vectorial sum of the radial and tangential velocities. Having imparted a large kinetic or velocity energy to the air, a large adiabatic compression takes place when the velocity is restored to its normal small values. The resultant pressure rise may be calculated by Bernoulli's equation or by the laws of thermodynamics, commonly expressed:

$$\frac{P_2}{P_1} = \left(\frac{\eta V^2}{6,088\, T_c} + 1\right)^{3.53}$$ (11:5)

P_1 and P_2 are the total head pressures at the entrance to and exit from the blower, respectively. ηV^2 is the effective impeller exit velocity squared and is a parameter varying only with impeller speed. T_c represents the entrance temperature in degrees Fahrenheit absolute. The

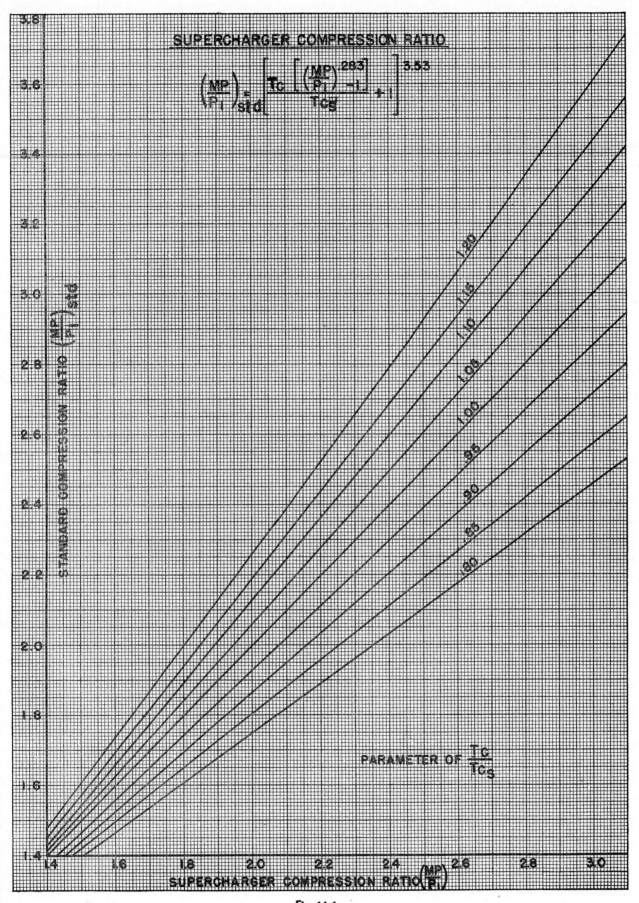

SUPERCHARGER COMPRESSION RATIO

$$\left(\frac{MP}{P_1}\right)_{std} = \left[\frac{T_C\left[\left(\frac{MP}{P_1}\right)^{.283}-1\right]}{T_{Cs}}+1\right]^{3.53}$$

STANDARD COMPRESSION RATIO $\left(\frac{MP}{P_1}\right)$/std

SUPERCHARGER COMPRESSION RATIO $\left(\frac{MP}{P_1}\right)$

PARAMETER OF $\frac{T_C}{T_{Cs}}$

1.20
1.15
1.10
1.05
1.00
.95
.90
.85
.80

Fig. 11:1a

53

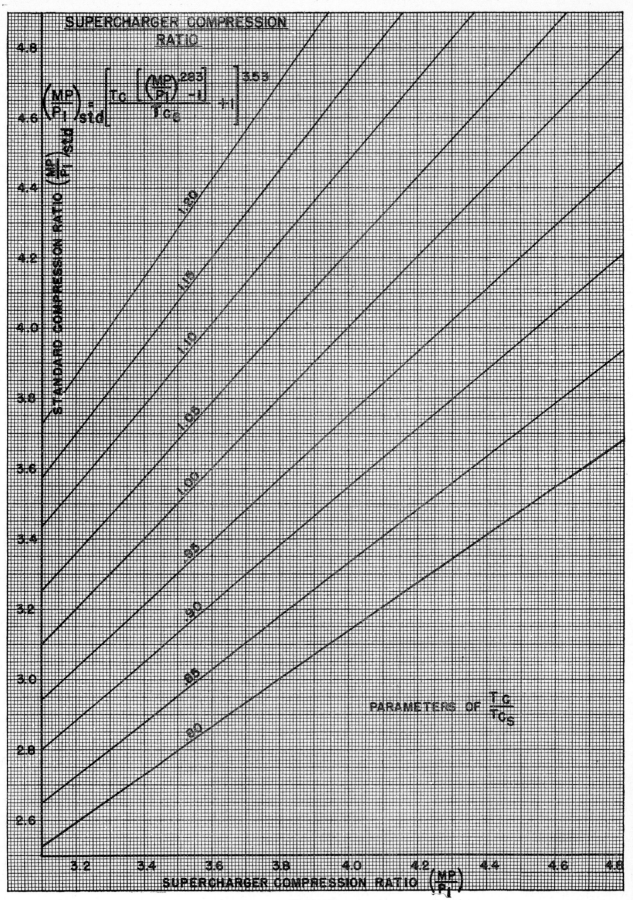

Fig. 11:1b

54

exponent is $\gamma/(\gamma - 1)$, where γ here is 1.395 in the temperature range of supercharged air.

Equation 11:5 may be written for standard carburetor air temperature, holding the tip speed parameter constant:

$$\frac{P_2}{P_1} = \left(\frac{\eta V^2}{6{,}088\, T_{c_s}} + 1\right)^{3.53} \qquad (11:6)$$

These two equations will combine to give a solution for standard compression ratio in terms of the actual compression ratio at T_c and the desired standard carburetor air temperature, T_{c_s}:

$$\left(\frac{P_2}{P_1}\right)_s = \left\{\frac{T_c}{T_{c_s}}\left[\left(\frac{P_2}{P_1}\right)^{.283} - 1\right] + 1\right\}^{3.53} \qquad (11:7)$$

For convenience, equation 11:7 has been plotted in Figures 11:1a and 11:1b. Knowing the compression ratio for any given inlet temperature, determined from power charts or by test measurement, then the manifold pressure for any reasonable variation of the inlet temperature will be given by this equation with reliable accuracy. If the blower handles dry air, equation 11:7 applies directly, but if fuel is injected into the air ahead of the blower, the entrance temperatures should be adjusted for the cooling effect of fuel vaporization according to the accepted empirical relation:

$$T_{\text{inlet}} = 15.95\,\sqrt{T_c} \text{ in } {}^\circ\text{K for } T_c > 254 \text{ only} \qquad (11:8)$$

For air temperatures below $-19{}^\circ\text{C}$, the fuel vaporization effect is apparently negligible, so the inlet temperature will not be affected by adding fuel.

Knowing how the manifold pressure varies with blower inlet temperature at *constant manifold temperature*, its effect on power will be expressed by:

$$\frac{\text{BHP}_s}{\text{BHP}} = \left(\frac{MP_s}{MP}\right)^a$$

at constant manifold temperature   (11:9)

where a is an empirical constant for a given engine and varies from 1.0 to 1.1 for different engines.

Taking into account the variation of brake horsepower with carburetor air temperature by the accepted square root power, the complete power correction is:

$$\frac{\text{BHP}_s}{\text{BHP}} = \left(\frac{MP_s}{MP}\right)^a \left(\frac{T_c}{T_{c_s}}\right)^{.5} \qquad (11:10)$$

Dividing equation 11:6 by equation 11:5, where P_1 is constant:

$$\frac{(P_2/P_1)_s}{P_2/P_1} = \frac{MP_s}{MP} = \left[\frac{\eta V^2/6{,}088\, T_{c_s} + 1}{\eta V^2/6{,}088\, T_c + 1}\right]^{3.53}$$

$$= \left[\frac{\eta V^2 + 6{,}088\, T_{c_s}}{\eta V^2 + 6{,}088\, T_c}\right]^{3.53}\left[\frac{T_c}{T_{c_s}}\right]^{3.53} \qquad (11:11)$$

This equation is observed to have two limits, such that

$$\frac{MP_s}{MP} = \left(\frac{T_c}{T_{c_s}}\right)^0 \quad \text{and} \quad \frac{MP_s}{MP} = \left[\frac{T_c}{T_{c_s}}\right]^{3.53} \qquad (11:12)$$

$$\eta V^2 \to \text{limit } 0 \qquad\qquad \eta V^2 \to \text{limit } \infty$$

This relationship suggests an approximation of the form

$$\frac{MP_s}{MP} = \left[\frac{T_c}{T_{c_s}}\right]^b \qquad (11:13)$$

where b is a function of ηV^2, which is proportional to the compression ratio.

Finally, equations 11:13 and 11:10 may be combined to obtain the simple result:

$$\frac{\text{BHP}_s}{\text{BHP}} = \left[\frac{T_c}{T_{c_s}}\right]^x\left[\frac{T_c}{T_{c_s}}\right]^{.5} = \left[\frac{T_c}{T_{c_s}}\right]^n \qquad (11:14)$$

The foregoing analysis makes it possible to investigate the range of values of the " over-all " exponent n throughout the range of compression ratios desired for both " wet " and " dry " compressions and for the normal range of brake horsepower versus manifold pressure characteristics of conventional engines. These results are presented in Figure 11:2 as the theoretical brake horsepower temperature correction exponent n for full throttle operation. This curve serves as a useful guide to the range of exponential values to be expected from various engines, and some of the calculated exponents in use are spotted on the curve.

If test stand data, or flight test data with a torquemeter, are available showing the variation of power with carburetor temperature only, they may be plotted and the value of n to fit equation 11:14 may be determined. Also, if such values for similar engines are plotted in Figure 11:2, they may be used as a guide in determining n for other engines. When such data are lacking, and judiciously choosing an n from Figure 11:2 is considered unsatisfactory, then it becomes necessary to use the specific engine power chart and, by

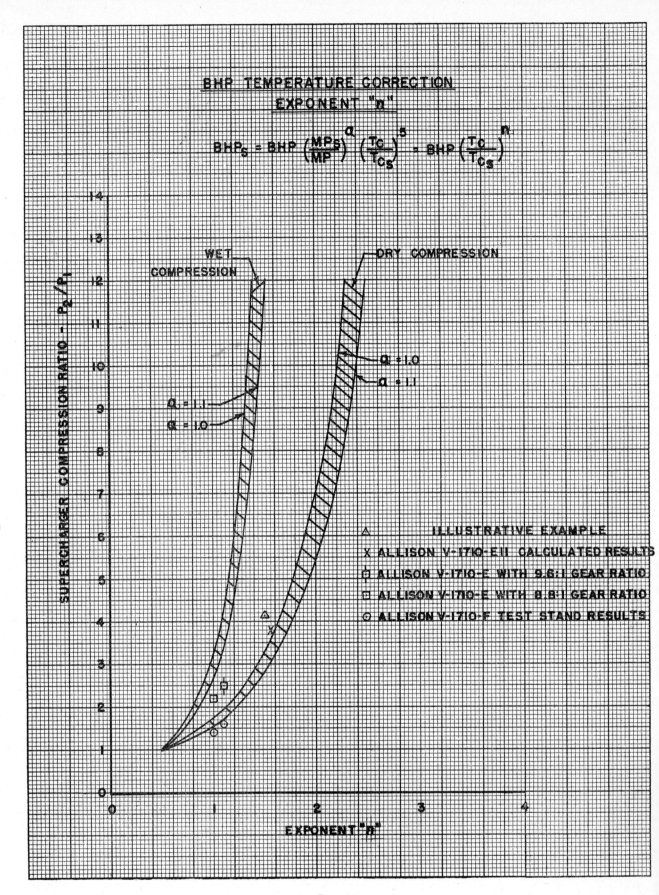

BHP TEMPERATURE CORRECTION
EXPONENT "n"

$$BHP_S = BHP \left(\frac{MP_S}{MP}\right)^a \left(\frac{T_C}{T_{CS}}\right)^5 = BHP \left(\frac{T_C}{T_{CS}}\right)^n$$

Fig. 11:2

applying the theory just described, investigate this phenomenon as outlined in the following paragraphs.

Given the power chart, select a point a few thousand feet above critical altitude, and, for the rpm in question, determine the compression ratio for the various stages. Note whether each com-

will vary linearly with the assumed carburetor temperature values.

If the brake horsepowers are now read directly from the power chart for the new manifold pressures thus determined, then the variation of chart brake horsepower with manifold pressure only is known, and the exponent x is calculated based on

TABLE 9.   DETERMINATION OF EXPONENT n

An engine is supercharged by two stages with fuel injection between stages and no intercooler or aftercooler. Auxiliary blower ratio is 8.1 (impeller diameter 9.5 in.) and main stage ratio is 6.85 (impeller diameter $12\frac{3}{16}$ in.). The engine delivers 1,011 brake horsepower for 3,000 rpm at 46 in. Hg manifold pressure at 26,000 ft. (All temperatures are in degrees Kelvin and manifold pressures in in. Hg.)

1. H_p	—	—	26,000	—	—
2. P_1 (atmospheric pressure)	—	—	10.62	—	—
3. P_x (cross-over pressure)	—	—	25.20	—	—
4. MP	—	—	44.00	—	—
5. T_c (atmospheric temperature)	—	—	237	—	—
6. T_x (cross-over temperature)	—	—	327	—	—
7. T_{c_s} (assumed)	217	227	—	247	257
8. T_c/T_{c_s}	1.092	1.044	—	.960	.922
9. P_x/P_1	—	—	2.37	—	—
10. P_{x_s}/P_1 (Figure 11:1a)	2.55	2.45	—	2.30	2.23
11. $P_{x_s} = (2)(10)$	27.10	26.02	—	24.43	23.70
12. $T_{x_s} = T_{c_s} + 90$	307	317	—	337	347
13. T_x/T_{x_s}	1.065	1.031	—	.971	.942
14. $(T_x'/T_{x_s}')^{.5}$ (for fuel: eq. 11:8)	1.032	1.016	—	.985	.970
15. MP/P_x	—	—	1.745	—	—
16. $(MP/P_x)_s$ (Figure 11:1a)	1.77	1.758	—	1.732	1.720
17. $MP_s = (11)(16)$	48.0	45.8	—	42.3	40.8
18. BHP_{ch} (from power chart)	—	—	1,020	—	—
19. BHP_{ch_s} (from power chart)	1112	1061	—	978	937
20. (19)/(18)	1.090	1.041	—	.959	.919
21. $x = \log(19)/\log(8)$	1.031	1.06	—	.98	.96
22. Average x	—	—	1.01	—	—
23. $n = x + .5$	—	—	1.51	—	—
24. CR = (9)(15)	—	—	4.14	—	—

For 3,000 rpm full throttle operation above critical altitude.

pression stage is wet or dry. Fuel injected directly into a blower entrance by means of a nozzle appears to pass through the blower with less atomization than that resulting from normal carburetion. This effect may be known for a given engine, in which case equation 11:8 will be modified, or kept in mind in selecting an " average " value of n.

Having read the standard chart power for the altitude selected and the standard carburetor entrance temperature, a range of temperatures within $\pm 25°C$ of the standard is arbitrarily assumed. By means of Figure 11:1 the new manifold pressures for each temperature may be deduced, keeping in mind that the temperature ratio applies to the compressor inlet conditions using equation 11:8 when it applies. Also, the temperature rise will remain constant through each blower, so the temperatures aft of each stage

the relations given in equations 11:9 and 11:13 by:

$$\frac{(BHP_{ch})_s}{BHP_{ch}} = \left(\frac{T_c}{T_{c_s}}\right)^x \qquad (11:15)$$

$$x = \frac{\log(BHP_{ch_s}/BHP_{ch})}{\log(T_c/T_{c_s})} \qquad (11:16)$$

Then $n = x + .5$ and this exponent is used in correcting actual full throttle flight test powers

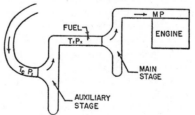

Fig. 11:3.   Engine two-stage blower induction system

to standard as illustrated in section 11.4. Figure 11:3 and Table 9 illustrate in detail the determination of n for a typical case.

11.4 Data Reduction

In the airplane installation, the carburetor air temperature will be higher than the atmospheric temperature by virtue of some temperature rise from adiabatic compression (similar to phenomenon described in Chapter 7), heating of the air scoop duct by the engine, and other causes. This temperature rise, a function of a given installa-

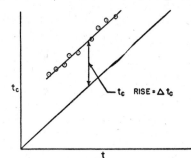

Fig. 11:4.   Carburetor air temperature variation

tion, must be paid for in loss of power. In other words, the carburetor air temperature will be above the atmospheric temperature by the

to what they would have been on a standard day by equation 11:14, remembering that the standard carburetor air temperature in this case is the standard atmospheric temperature plus the carburetor air temperature rise from Figure 11:4. Plot the standard powers against standard density ratio (or on the engine power chart) and read critical altitude as that altitude at which rated power obtains. Figure 11:5 illustrates results obtained on a hot day, case (1), and on a cold day, case (2), at different altitudes reduced to standard by the method described.

As a guide in reducing the data, an outline of the steps is given below:

(a) Given H_p, rpm (rated), MP_m, t_c from flight test for one level flight, *full throttle* run.

(b) From the power chart read the *chart power*, BHP_{ch}, for the test values of H_p, rpm, and MP.

(c) Calculate the actual power, BHP, by $BHP = BHP_{ch} \ (T_s/T_c)^{.5}$, where temperatures are absolute values of actual carburetor air temperature and standard atmospheric temperature

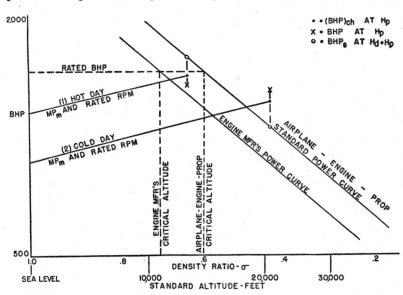

Fig. 11:5.   Illustration of correction of test brake horsepower to standard conditions from a "hot" day and a "cold" day

amount of this temperature rise and must be tolerated. The actual carburetor air temperature versus the actual free air temperature as shown in Figure 11:4 is easily determined by plotting from full throttle, high power, level flight test runs.

The next step is to determine the actual powers from the *full throttle*, rated rpm, level flight test runs at various altitudes (from torquemeter or power curves). Then correct these actual powers

corresponding to the pressure altitude. In the case of a torquemeter, BHP is available directly.

(d) Determine the inherent carburetor air temperature rise. (If it varies read it from Figure 11:4 at standard atmospheric temperature.) Add this rise to the standard atmospheric temperature to get what would be the standard carburetor air temperature, designated T_{c_s}, on a standard day, converting to absolute units = °C + 273.

(e) Calculate the standard power on a standard day by $BHP_s = BHP\,(T_c/T_{c_s})^n$, where n has already been determined for this blower system and engine rpm.

(f) Plot BHP_s versus σ corresponding to the standard altitude, which is the same as H_p since the effect of the nonstandard temperature has been corrected to standard.

(g) Determine the critical altitude corresponding to σ at the rated power.

11.5 Data Required

Any change in drag condition of the airplane seriously affecting its speed, or any change in carburetor air scoop design or location, will influence the effect of ram and require a new flight test determination of critical altitude. Required data are as follows:

Rated rpm
Full throttle
Level flight

H_{p_r}
RPM_r
MP_r
t_{c_r}
t_r
V_r

At least four pressure altitudes near critical and several at high altitudes. This will define complete full throttle altitude power variation useful in maximum speed versus altitude determination and permit more accurate fairing and extrapolation of the curve and more accurate comparison with the engine power curve. Also, fairing of a climb full throttle power curve between these two curves will be more accurate.

Notes: It may take five minutes of continuous operation to obtain stabilized conditions during each run.

A complete check of the airspeed line system for leaks must be made before and after each flight.

CHAPTER 12

UNIVERSAL SPEED-POWER POLAR

12.1 Introduction

The universal speed-power polar is not in common use at the present time because of the troublesome complication of propulsive efficiency from one point of view or the amount of flight testing necessary from another. From the standpoint of urgency during wartime, only critical or maximum performance items are of crucial importance, and detailed investigation of performance applicable to commercial operation is relatively limited. Consequently, this chapter is included only for the sake of thoroughness as a method of complete performance evaluation which will probably find extensive use in peacetime.

At present there is no method of measuring propulsive efficiency in flight, and calculations are laborious and of questionable accuracy. In lieu of being able to evaluate this variable, which would simplify flight testing tremendously, considerable test data must be obtained. An excellent presentation of this subject is found in reference 14.

12.2 Effect of Density on Power Required

As outlined in previous sections, the engine differentiates between the temperature and the pressure of the air at a given density and delivers power accordingly. However, both the propeller and the airplane operate according to aerodynamic laws in which the air forces generated depend only on the density property of the air, except for Mach number limitations. The thrust horsepower required by the airplane at standard gross weight in level flight is expressed by the well-known equation:

$$THP_{req} = \frac{C_{D_p}\sigma S V^3}{146,600} + \left(\frac{W_s}{ekb}\right)^2 \frac{1}{3.01\ V\sigma}$$

$$= \eta BHP \quad (12:1)$$

For convenience written

$$THP = C_1 \sigma V^3 + \frac{C_2}{\sigma V} \quad (12:2)$$

where

$$C_1 = \frac{C_{D_p} S}{146,600}$$

$$C_2 = \frac{(W_s)^2}{3.01\ (ekb)^2}$$

Multiplying both sides of the equation by $\sqrt{\sigma}$ gives

$$THP\ \sqrt{\sigma} = C_1 (V\ \sqrt{\sigma})^3 + C_2/(V\ \sqrt{\sigma}) \quad (12:3)$$

Equation 12:3 reveals that a single plot of $THP\ \sqrt{\sigma}$ versus $V\ \sqrt{\sigma}$ for a given airplane is independent of density, which is a very convenient phenomenon.

The accuracy of equation 12:1 depends upon the range of speeds (usually down to a speed corresponding to about $.8\ C_{L_{max}}$) for which the given value of e is valid. Here, e is the square root of Oswald's span efficiency factor, usually determined from a plot of C_D versus C_L^2 from wind tunnel model tests. Throughout most of the range, a straight line may be faired through the tests points from which:

$$e = \left[\frac{(\Delta C_L)^2}{\pi R (\Delta C_D)}\right]^{1/2} \quad (12:4)$$

Values of e will change with various airplane configurations, such as landing flap deflection.

The parasite drag coefficient, C_{D_p}, is determined as the drag coefficient, C_D, at $C_L = 0$, by extrapolation of the straight line C_D versus C_L^2. Since C_{D_p} from wind tunnel model tests is inaccurate, it is usually approximated more closely after flight test data are available by solving for it in equation 12:1, using flight tests values, usually for V_{max}. Propulsive efficiency must be estimated by calculation in order to determine the thrust horsepower from the actual brake horsepower.

$$THP = \eta(BHP) \qquad (12:5)$$

12.3 Effect of Gross Weight on Power Required

By inspection of equations 12:1 and 12:3, the thrust horsepower required at any gross weight other than standard may be written:

$$THP \sqrt{\sigma} = C_1(V \sqrt{\sigma})^3 + \frac{C_2(W/W_s)^2}{(V \sqrt{\sigma})} \qquad (12:6)$$

If both sides of this expression are then multiplied by $(W_s/W)^{3/2}$, the following equation will be obtained:

$$\frac{THP \sqrt{\sigma}}{(W/W_s)^{3/2}} = C_1 \left(\frac{V \sqrt{\sigma}}{\sqrt{W/W_s}}\right)^3$$
$$+ \frac{C_2 V \sqrt{\sigma}}{\sqrt{W/W_s}} \qquad (12:7)$$

This equation signifies that a plot of $THP \sqrt{\sigma}/(W/W_s)^{3/2}$ versus $V \sqrt{\sigma}/\sqrt{W/W_s}$ is independent of both altitude and gross weight.

12.4 Universal Speed-Power Polar

Until a satisfactory thrustmeter is available for use in conjunction with a torquemeter, it will be impossible to determine propulsive efficiency from flight test. For this reason, it is better to keep all flight test data in terms of brake horsepower. Therefore, if equation 12:7 is divided by the propulsive efficiency, η, which is a function of BHP, V, rpm, and σ for a given engine-body-propeller combination, the result is

$$P_w \sqrt{\sigma} = \frac{C_1}{\eta}(V_w\sqrt{\sigma})^3 + \frac{C_2/\eta}{V_w \sqrt{\sigma}} \qquad (12:8)$$

Where

$$P_w \sqrt{\sigma} = \frac{BHP \sqrt{\sigma}}{(W/W_s)^{3/2}} \qquad (12:9)$$

$$V_w \sqrt{\sigma} = \frac{V \sqrt{\sigma}}{(W/W_s)^{1/2}} \qquad (12:10)$$

This equation shows that a plot of $P_w \sqrt{\sigma}$ versus $V_w \sqrt{\sigma}$ would be independent of altitude and gross weight also, if C_1/η and C_2/η remained constant. Unfortunately, here the simplification of the speed-power relationship ceases, since propulsive efficiency varies not only with the quantities expressed in equation 12:8, but also with

another variable, namely rpm. As a result, considerable flight testing must be resorted to in order to establish speed-power curves for a family of rpm parameters to determine the level flight performance throughout the complete flight range of the airplane-engine-propeller combination.

If the rpm parameter is introduced in the form

$$N_w \sqrt{\sigma} = \frac{(\text{propeller rpm}) \sqrt{\sigma}}{(W/W_s)^{1/2}} \qquad (12:11)$$

typical universal speed-power polars from a series of level flight runs at different altitudes and/or rpm's will appear as shown in Figure 12:1.

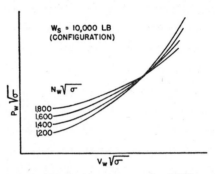

Fig. 12:1.   Universal speed-power level flight polars

Unfortunately, test points cannot be obtained at constant values of $N_w \sqrt{\sigma}$, hence cross plotting and judicious fairing must be employed.

The reason for choosing the rpm parameter using the same function of density and weight used in the speed term is that each individual $N_w \sqrt{\sigma}$ parameter becomes universally applicable. This is explained in the following paragraphs.

For a given propeller-body combination, propulsive efficiency, η, may be determined as a function of only two parameters, namely propeller V/ND and power coefficient expressed:

$$C_P = \frac{C_3}{D^5}\frac{BHP}{(N \sqrt{\sigma})^2 N} = \frac{C_4 BHP}{(N \sqrt{\sigma})^2 N} \qquad (12:12)$$

The fact that any one point on any one of the speed-power curves is independent of altitude may be explained by assuming two altitudes such that the $\sqrt{\sigma}$ at the second is half that at the first. Then at the second altitude the true speed is double that at the first, and likewise, the true propeller rpm is double, for the same parameter values. This results in the same V/ND at both altitudes. Likewise, the true power is doubled for constant $P_w \sqrt{\sigma}$. Determining the power coefficient by equation 12:12 shows that for the same $N\sqrt{\sigma}$ doubling the power in the numerator cancels doubling the propeller rpm in the denominator, and C_P remains constant. Therefore, the propulsive efficiency is the same at both altitudes, and the point in question applies to any altitude for the given parameter values. This fact may be seen in equation 12:8 wherein C_1/η and C_2/η have been proved to be constant for any change in altitude density ratio.

If the same line of reasoning is applied to the weight variation, it will be seen that again the true speed and rpm vary identically to produce a constant V/ND.

Also, the fact that any one point on any one of the speed-power curves is independent of gross weight may be explained in a similar manner. Assume two gross weights such that the square root of the gross weight ratio for the second weight is twice that of the first. Then for constant parameter values the true speed and true rpm are both doubled, leaving V/ND constant. However, the true power for the second gross weight is $(2)^3$ times that for the first gross weight. This effect is again cancelled in the equation for C_P as rpm appears cubed in the denominator, so again C_P is constant as seen from equation 12:12 rewritten for convenience at a constant altitude as

$$C_P = \frac{C_3}{\sigma D^5}\frac{\text{BHP}}{N^3} = \frac{C_5\text{BHP}}{N^3} \qquad (12:13)$$

Thus, when all available flight test data for level flight are reduced and plotted in universal speed-power polar form, they become applicable to any and all level flight conditions within the range of the parameters. These speed-power polars can be used for determining any desired level flight performance, such as maximum speeds, cruising speeds, or range and endurance when the additional specific fuel consumption data are available.

It must be emphasized that the *standard gross weight*, W_s, used in the parameter determinations of the polars and the *configuration of the airplane* at which the tests were run, must be noted on the curves. Otherwise, these polars are meaningless. Inspection of the foregoing equations outlining the theory upon which the universal speed-power curves are based reveals the important variables.

For instance, any change in external appearance or shape of the airplane, such as armament changes, landing gear or flap positions, windows open or closed, painted or unpainted surfaces, and auxiliary tanks on or off, will affect the parasite drag coefficient, C_{D_p}, and thereby alter and displace previously determined speed-power polars. It is, therefore, necessary to keep an accurate log of the configuration of any given airplane throughout all flight testing if intelligent and accurate flight test results are expected.

Since the rpm parameter is based upon propeller rpm, an internal change of the engine-propeller gear ratio will not affect the universal speed-power polars, but changing the propeller design obviously will. Changing engine output by introducing a new engine-supercharger gear ratio will not noticeably affect the curves.

Location of the center of gravity will have a slight affect on the curves inasmuch as a slightly different position of control surfaces will be required to trim the airplane. Ordinarily, this will cause no concern.

It should be kept in mind that this theory does not apply for conditions in which the critical Mach number is appreciably exceeded by any portion of the airplane. At high speeds and high altitudes, the propeller tips may be operating within this region, in which case the effect of compressibility will cause a loss in propulsive efficiency and the power co-ordinate on the speed-power polar will be displaced upward.

12.5 Data Reduction

Data reduction is very simple. Previous sections have outlined the method of determining BHP, $V\sqrt{\sigma}$, and σ from flight test data. Given the values of rpm, gear ratio (GR), W, and the standard gross weight of the airplane, W_s, the steps involved are to:

(a) Calculate $(W/W_s)^{1/2}$.

(b) Calculate $(W/W_s)^{3/2}$.

(c) Calculate $P_w\sqrt{\sigma} = \text{BHP}\sqrt{\sigma}/(W/W_s)^{3/2}$.

(d) Calculate $V_w\sqrt{\sigma} = V\sqrt{\sigma}/(W/W_s)^{1/2}$.

(e) Calculate propeller rpm $= N =$ (engine rpm) (GR).

(f) Calculate $N_w \sqrt{\sigma} = N \sqrt{\sigma}/(W/W_s)^{1/2}$.

(g) Plot $P_w \sqrt{\sigma}$ versus $V_w \sqrt{\sigma}$.

(h) Fair lines through all tests points at constant $N_w \sqrt{\sigma}$.

At least five or six points, preferably more, at the same altitude and rpm are required to determine a faired curve. Values of $N_w \sqrt{\sigma}$ will vary slightly, making it a little difficult to fair curves for constant values. In the future, a method of correcting such values, based on propeller theory, to identical values for small changes may be presented.

12.6 Data Required

V_r
RPM_r
MP_r
H_{p_r}
t_{c_r}
t_r
W
Configuration

Level flight throughout speed range for each altitude and each rpm, not less than five runs, and as wide a range of altitudes and rpm as possible.

Notes: If at all possible, fuel consumption data should also be obtained during these tests.

A complete check of the airspeed line system for leaks must be made before and after each flight.

CHAPTER 13

MAXIMUM SPEED DETERMINATION

13.1 Discussion

Maximum speed must be qualified by specification, and the specification requirements are airplane configuration, flight attitude, gross weight, altitude, brake horsepower, and rpm. That the atmospheric conditions are standard at the specified altitude is always implied, and level flight attitude is usually assumed inasmuch as it is of the greatest importance.

Thus, a maximum speed quotation with the omission of any one of these specifications loses its significance. Section 12.6 presents the flight test data for all of the required variables. Maximum power and rpm ratings versus altitude are specified by the engine manufacturer. These power specifications apply up to the airplane-propeller-engine critical altitude, but at this altitude and above, the standard rated power has been determined from flight test in Chapter 11. Hence, the specified maximum rated power and rpm available to produce maximum speed at any altitude is determined from the preceding sections to be as illustrated in Figure 13:1.

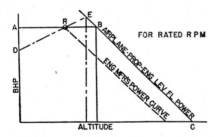

Fig. 13:1. Comparison of brake horsepower available on a test stand and in flight

R is the engine manufacturer's power rating conditions. Normally the power rating down to sea level is constant, in which case curve ABC is the power curve for the basis of maximum speed determination. Sometimes the engine manufacturer's specific power limitation is based on constant manifold pressure, line DR. In the latter case, power curve DEC is used, in which case critical altitude will be lowered and the power at this critical altitude will be increased.

Airplane maximum speeds will vary considerably between successive production airplanes and also for the same airplane over a period of time. This is partly attributable to accumulations of minor external airplane changes or additions, variations in workmanship and fitting of cowl panels and fillets, service wear, damage, accumulation of dirt, and propeller surface deterioration with service, and partly to engine service condition and wear. Variables affecting engine operation have been mentioned at the end of section 10.4, and when it is realized that power for a given engine is determined from power charts derived from tests of some other " typical " engine by the method given in Chapter 10, the accuracy of such power determination is obviously questionable. In the case of torquemeter power determination, the results are generally very reliable.

A third major variable may be described as the human element, which includes technique. The accuracy of observed data will depend upon the instrumentation and its accuracy of calibration, the skill of the pilot in obtaining steady equilibrium flight conditions, and the accuracy of data recording.

Fourth is the inevitable atmospheric conditions aptly described in the following quotation from reference 14:

The atmosphere is a sea of air in which man has, after many years, managed to navigate unsupported by solid connection to the earth or by means of any appreciable buoyancy of simple displacement. This sea is not quiescent but is ever in turmoil under the forces of thermo- and aero-dynamics that visibly produce our weather. It may flow as a tumbling waterfall over the mountainous areas or become a turbulent, rolling, seething mass, or flow smoothly and quietly with unappreciable ripple. The air currents may be made visible by the clouds they produce, or by the smoke, dust, soil, and sand that they lift and carry. Even if visible, the magnitude of their effect is not directly apparent. Visible, or not visible, the effect of air currents has been frequently ignored in determining airplane performance. The way in which air currents affect the performance of an airplane is well illustrated by the feats of soaring.

Realizing the existence of these possible inaccuracies, it is unreasonable to base speed run results on one test point; in fact, in the long run, it may be misleading and expensive in both time and money. Therefore, rather extensive and complete flight test determination of a speed-power polar is highly desirable for the standard airplane.

Often the relatively small effect of added drag items on maximum speed is desired, and for such tests not less than four speed runs for one speed-power polar curve should be accepted. It is also highly desirable to make consecutive flight tests without, with, and then without a small or important configuration change in question as a further check for substantiation of the original polar, since a small difference between two high-speed values is being sought. This procedure is particularly recommended where a torquemeter is not available.

Complete speed-power curves for the standard airplane will also permit a minimum of testing for a new configuration, as the original curves will be very useful as a guide in the fairing of new curves.

13.2 Universal Polar Method

In this case, it is merely necessary to enter the universal speed-power curves with the specified variables and determine the true speeds outlined as follows:

For each altitude the following procedure is used in the determination of maximum speed:

Given: BHP, RPM, Altitude, W, GR.

Refer to the proper universal speed-power polar (Figure 12:1, section 12.4).

(a) Calculate $(W/W_s)^{1/2}$; W_s is noted on curve.

(b) Calculate $(W/W_s)^{3/2}$.

(c) Determine σ for the standard density altitude given (Figure 8:3) and the standard BHP (section 11.4).

(d) Calculate $P_w \sqrt{\sigma} = \mathrm{BHP}\, \sqrt{\sigma}/(W/W_s)^{3/2}$.

(e) Calculate $N = (\mathrm{RPM})\,(\mathrm{GR})$.

(f) Calculate $N_w \sqrt{\sigma} = N \sqrt{\sigma}/(W/W_s)^{1/2}$.

(g) Read $V_w \sqrt{\sigma}$ from the curve for items (d) and (f).

(h) $V_{\max} = (V_w \sqrt{\sigma})(W/W_s)^{1/2}/\sqrt{\sigma} = $ mph.

Obtain these maximum speeds for all altitudes for which data are available and plot altitude versus maximum speed, $V_{\max}$. A typical plot is shown for a two-stage or two-speed supercharger engine in Figure 13:2.

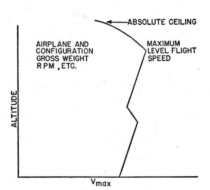

Fig. 13:2.   Typical variation of maximum level flight speed with altitude

13.3 Conventional Polar Method

The conventional plot of actual brake horsepower versus true airspeed is commonly used to determine maximum speed for a given set of specific conditions. Referring back to equation 12:1, it is obvious that such a plot holds only for the density altitude at which the data were obtained. Furthermore, it is limited by the propulsive efficiency conditions, which means it holds only for the rpm employed as well as the density.

Gross weight is also an influencing variable. However, when the weight variation for the test points is less than 10 per cent of the gross weight, this effect on high speeds is small and generally neglected. Since the slower the speed the greater the effect of weight changes on speed (see the last term of the equation), increasing successive speeds should be employed during speed-power polar runs. That is, run the low-speed point with full fuel first, and at the higher speeds where the gross weight is furthest from standard due to fuel consumption, its effect will be minimized in the over-all curve. Sometimes it is expedient to overload the airplane so that during speed runs the average gross weight will be closer to the standard value. Note also that at high altitudes, low density ratios, consideration of gross weight variation becomes even more important.

If it becomes necessary to make a correction

for weight, a method may be derived from equations 12:1 and 12:2 for any gross weight. Given the true airspeed at the given altitude for the particular gross weight as tested, the speed may be adjusted for the gross weight correction at constant thrust horsepower. This implies that propulsive efficiency also remains constant, and the error involved is considered negligible. The rate of change of equivalent airspeed with gross weight on this basis for reasonable gross weight changes will be, in engineering units:

$$\frac{\Delta V \sqrt{\sigma}}{\Delta W} = \frac{2 W V \sqrt{\sigma}}{W^2 - 3 C_1 (V \sqrt{\sigma})^4 / C_6} \quad (13:1)$$

where

$$C_1 = \frac{C_{D_p} S}{146,600} \quad \text{and} \quad C_6 = \frac{1}{3.01 (ekb)^2} = C_2 / W_s^2$$

$$(13:2)$$

(For C_1 and C_2, see section 12.2.)

Note that this expression is not valid at the lower speeds where e will not apply as mentioned in section 12.2. For convenience equation 13:1 may be calculated and plotted as $\Delta V \sqrt{\sigma} / \Delta W$ versus $V \sqrt{\sigma}$ for parameters of gross weight. It then becomes a simple matter to correct the flight test speed result to its new value for any given standard gross weight, the speed that would be obtained at the same brake horsepower but at the new weight.

Speed runs should be made under favorable atmospheric conditions. Rough air should be avoided and the test area selected should be well away from scattered cloud formations. It is also good practice to determine the atmospheric lapse rate in the altitude vicinity at which the runs are made as a further possible check on undesirable or unusual atmospheric conditions.

In general, it will take some five minutes of flying at constant observed engine and atmospheric conditions to establish the equilibrium level flight speed. Often test pilots approach the test level from above or below with set engine conditions in order to arrive at the approximate equilibrium speed in level flight. Obviously the airplane must accelerate or decelerate in approaching the equilibrium speed, and the closer it is approached the smaller the incremental acceleration force becomes. This process can be carried too far as the relationship is asymptotic,

and, actually, the gross weight is constantly diminishing.

A form similar to that illustrated at the end of this chapter is convenient for outlining the airplane configuration in a flight test report. Calculations involved in the determination of a typical speed-power polar and a diagram, Figure 13:3, are presented in Table 10. This curve is

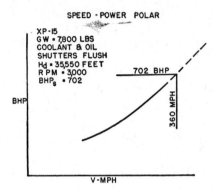

Fig. 13:3.   Typical level flight speed-power polar

extrapolated, if necessary, to higher values in case the standard power could not be obtained in flight (on a hot day). Standard brake horsepower has been calculated for the single full throttle point, but a better average value should be taken from the previously determined curve of standard brake horsepower versus altitude. For this standard power, the maximum speed for standard conditions at the density altitude is read from Figure 13:3. The power, rpm, altitude, gross weight, and airplane configuration conditions for this speed should be quoted with it. Repeating the process for a sufficient number of altitudes will provide data for plotting $V_{\max}$ versus altitude as diagrammed in Figure 13:2.

If the test runs are desired at critical altitude, the altitude at which that density exists may be located with sufficient accuracy in flight. Altitude and free air temperature may be read from the instruments at a low airspeed, to avoid a large temperature error, and spotted on Figure 8:3. By trial and error the proper altitude can readily be found.

13.4 Speed-Power Polar Data Reduction

Table 10 illustrates typical calculations for four-speed runs. The full throttle brake horsepower reduced to standard is used to supplement full throttle engine power data at other pressure altitudes.

TABLE 10. MAXIMUM SPEED DETERMINATION — DATA REDUCTION

$H_{pr}{}^*$	ft	35,410	35,400	35,380	35,360	Observed data.
H_{pm}	ft	35,200	35,190	35,170	35,150	Corr. for lab. inst. cal. error.
H_p	ft	35,390	35,340	35,295	35,260	Corr. for position error for V_m.
$V_r{}^*$	mph	197	186	174	161	Observed data.
V_m	mph	199	188	176	163	Corr. for lab. inst. cal. error.
V_{cal}	mph	203	192	179	166	Corr. for position error for V_m.
$t_r{}^*$	°C	−42	−43	−45	−44	Observed data.
t_m	°C	−44	−45	−47	−46	Corr. for lab. inst. cal. error.
M	—	.540	.511	.478	.444	From Figure 8:1.
K	—	.75	.75	.75	.75	Free air pickup constant (sect. 7.3.)
$M\sqrt{K}$	—	.468	.443	.414	.384	
t	°C	−53	−53	−54	−52	Figure 8:2.
V_c	mph	664	664	663	666	Figure 8:2.
V	mph	359	340	317	296	$V = MV_c$.
Average H_D	ft	35,500	—	—	—	Figure 8:3.
Throttle	—	full	part	part	part	Full or part throttle operation.
RPM*	—	3,000	3,000	3,000	3,000	Engine rpm — no instrument error.
$MP_r{}^*$	in. Hg	32.5	28.8	26	23	Observed data.
MP_m	in. Hg	32.3	28.6	25.8	22.9	Corr. for lab. inst. cal. error.
BHP_{ch}	—	720	612	525	449	From engine power chart (MP, RPM, H_p).
$t_{cr}{}^*$	°C	−38	−40	−41	−41	Observed data.
t_c	°C	−39	−41	−42	−42	Corr. for lab. inst. cal. error.
t_s	°C	−55	−55	−55	−55	Standard atmospheric temperature at H_p.
$(T_s/T_c)^{.5}$	—	.966	.970	.972	.972	$(t_s + 273)^{.5}/(t_c + 273)^{.5}$.
BHP	—	696	594	510	436	$BHP = BHP_{ch}\,(T_s/T_c)^{.5}$.
W	lb	7,270	7,295	7,360	7,445	From plot of GW vs. time.
Δt_c	°C	14	—	—	—	Carburetor air rise $= t_c - t$.
t_{cs}	°C	−41	—	—	—	$t_s + \Delta t_c$.
$(T_c/T_{cs})^n$	—	1.013	—	—	—	Absolute units ($n = 1.35$).
BHP_s	—	706	—	—	—	$BHP_s = BHP\,(T_c/T_{cs})^{1.35}$.
BHP_s at H_D	—	702	—	—	—	From plot of BHP_s vs. H_p.

*Flight test data required.

The method given in the table ignores the separate effect of jet exhaust thrust which most present day airplanes attempt to employ. This effect is included in the over-all speed-power polar and, though strictly incorrect, is acceptable. Jet thrust horsepower is small relative to the brake horsepower. However, in calculating propulsive efficiency for the maximum speed-power data and in determining the airplane parasite drag coefficient, this item should be considered. Jet thrust effect will also have some bearing on the universal speed-power polar method, but it has not been investigated.

FLIGHT TEST CONFIGURATION

AIRPLANE

Airplane **Baricuda** Model **XP-15** Serial No **AC41-18762**
Wing Area **260 ft²** Wing Span **45 ft.** Des. Wt. Empty **7800 lbs.**
Standard G. W. **8200 lbs.** C. G. **26.0%** Fuel Cap. **150 gal.**
Oil Cap. **15 gal.** Prestone Cap. **18 gal.** Cannon **20 mm.**
Fuselage Guns **3 50 cal.** Blast Tubes **Cone type**
Wing Guns **None** Blast Tubes **None**
Bomb Rack **and 500# bomb** External Tank **None**
Antennae **Fin to aft fuselage** Antenna Mast **None**
Surface Condition **bare alclad**
Flaps **Plain** Flap Deflection **50°**
Airspeed Head **Shark fin-wing boom** Airspeed Ind. **Kolls. 589K-06-103**
Altimeter **AC42-18854** M P Gauge **AC75596**
Tachometer **AC 48773** Oat Indicator **30 (free air)**
Oat Pickup **8A (free air)** Cat Pickup **44 (carb. air)**
Special Instrumentation

Other Configuration
1. Laminar flow wing 66 2 x-118
2. Resistance type free air temp pickup under left wing
3. Camera lens left wing L.E.
4. Landing gear flipper door fairings removed

ENGINE

Manufacturer **Continental** Model **V-3420** Serial No. **2**
Mfg. Spec. **178x** Impeller Diam. **9.5"** Impeller G. R. **9.5:1**
T. O. Rating **1400/3000/S.L.** Mil Rating **1300/3000/26000**
Norm. Rating **1200/2600/25000** Comp. Ratio **7.8:1**
Carburetor **Stromberg PT 25 F-11** Serial No. **13428**
Exhaust Stacks **Std. 6 port - area 6 in.²**
Fuel Used **AN-F-28 Grade 130**

PROPELLER

Manufacturer **Curtiss** Blade Design **A60-197**
No of Blades **4** Diameter **11'6"** Gear Ratio **2.5:1**
High Pitch **75°** Low Pitch **20°**

Form 13-13

CHAPTER 14

CLIMB PERFORMANCE

14.1 Discussion

The forces acting on an airplane in level flight and in climb at the same airspeeds may be represented by Figures 14:1 and 14:2.

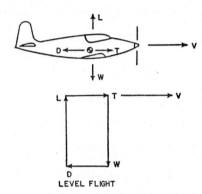

Fig. 14:1.   Forces acting in level flight

In the level flight case, the lift equals the weight and the thrust balances the drag, resulting in an equilibrium of forces. If the thrust force is re-

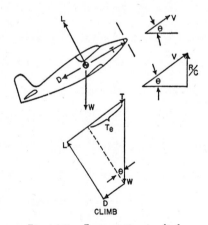

Fig. 14:2.   Forces acting in climb

duced, the excess drag force will cause the airplane to decelerate to a lower speed at which the drag value will equal the thrust available. If the thrust is increased, the converse is true. However, if the thrust is increased and the airspeed is to be held constant, the nose must be pulled up into a

climbing attitude, in which case a given climb angle will be obtained such that the excess thrust is used in maintaining this attitude.

The vectorial sum of the forces in climb is shown in Figure 14:2. In climb calculations, the lift is assumed equal to the weight, and the drag as calculated includes the induced drag due to this lift. As discerned from the diagram, a vectorial sum of these assumed forces would not represent equilibrium conditions, as the figure will not close. For the relatively small climbing angles of conventional aircraft, the maximum error in calculated maximum rate of climb in neglecting the climb angle is approximately 3 per cent.

The major difference between the climb vectorial forces and those in level flight is caused by the excess thrust over that required to overcome the drag force as indicated in the figure. This excess thrust, in fact, defines the climb angle, as may be easily visualized by picturing the figure for various thrust magnitudes, assuming the thrust to act in the flight path direction. Knowing the climb angle, then the sine of the angle times the flight path velocity gives the vertical velocity, or rate of climb. Again in the rate of climb expression as always used, the sine of the climb angle is taken as equal to the excess thrust divided by the gross weight.

$$R/C = 88\ V \sin \theta = \frac{88\ VT_e}{W} = \frac{33,000\ \text{EHP}}{W}$$

$$(14:1)$$

At present neglecting all of the trigonometric functions arising from the angle of climb is commonly accepted, but as climb performance is further improved, these refinements wi'l become necessary. In flight testing, aerodynamic calculations are used only as a guide in making small corrections to observed performance in reducing to standard conditions, so these errors will be insignificant. It may be noted here that the effect of exhaust jet thrust should not be overlooked in climb calculations, especially at the higher altitudes where the brake horsepower available decreases in magnitude. Another factor, not as important, is acceleration in the flight path direction arising from the variation of true airspeed with altitude for optimum climbing conditions.

Under given conditions there will be one airspeed at which the maximum rate of climb for a given power will obtain, but above or below which the rate of climb will diminish. Determination of this best climbing airspeed at one altitude involves making several climbs at different airspeeds and constant power in order to obtain a plot of rate of climb versus airspeed. From such a curve the maximum rate of climb and the airspeed required to obtain it are determined for each altitude tested. The main purpose of running saw-tooth climbs (the flight history on a barograph looks like a series of steps or saw teeth in making repeated climbs and descents through the small altitude range investigated), then, is to obtain the standard optimum climbing airspeed and the standard power and their variations with altitude. These results will then provide a

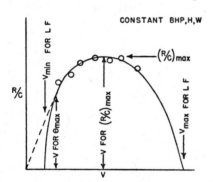

Fig. 14:3. Variation of rate of climb with airspeed

schedule of optimum conditions for making a continuous climb to service ceiling at the maximum climbing rate. Figures 14:3 and 14:4 illustrate the significance of a series of saw-tooth climb points and the determination of best climbing airspeed versus altitude from a series of them.

For military operation, maximum climb performance, that is, climb at maximum rated power, is the focus of interest. A complete universal rate of climb-speed curve similar to the universal speed-power polar would be desirable for commercial airplanes, but is not of sufficient value under emergency conditions to warrant this

expenditure of time. However, the universal method will be outlined in order that the range of the curves may be extended if further testing should be necessary or is available. In determination of maximum range, economical climb at low powers should be determined, but since this phase of a long flight is relatively unimportant, the extensive testing is usually omitted. However, some of the high altitude universal rate-of-climb-speed curves will be useful in such determination at low altitudes, since the same curve will represent low powers and rpm's at the low altitude densities.

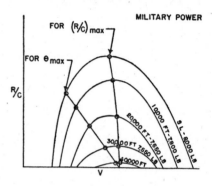

Fig. 14:4. Variation of rate of climb with airspeed and altitude

In order for saw-tooth climbs to be directly comparable, each climb at the same altitude must be corrected to standard conditions and to a standard gross weight, since the gross weight is varying throughout the flight. When a full climb to ceiling is made (Chapter 15), take-off is made with standard gross weight, and no weight correction is applied since the reduction in weight with consumption of fuel is a standard condition.

The caution in deciding whether or not weather conditions are suitable for climb tests cannot be overemphasized. It will be found that consistent results from two different climb tests will be difficult to obtain. Climb performance will be greatly affected by wind gradients, up or down drafts, lapse rates, turbulence, or other unusual atmospheric conditions. Saw teeth should be made only in very smooth air in carefully selected atmospheric conditions. The atmosphere will usually become fairly stable and uniform at night, but during the daytime and with temperature changes, the conditions of the atmosphere will usually become unsuitable at one or more altitude ranges. For this reason, it is strongly recommended that climbs to ceiling for data purposes should be made as close to sunrise as possible, at which time the best atmospheric conditions are usually encountered. Sometimes the late evening is also a good time to operate. Continuous climb results made during midday or afternoon are more often erratic and unsatisfactory than not.

As an illustration of possible atmospheric effects on climb performance, assume a horizontal current of air having a velocity gradient dV_w/dH in the vertical plane. An airplane flying at velocity V will experience a horizontal acceleration relative to the air $(dV_w/dH)(R/C)$ in flying through these horizontal air strata. The rate of change of energy will be expressed by the product of the airplane's mass, acceleration, and velocity. If instead of allowing this energy to change the airplane velocity, it is converted into a change in rate of climb the equation will be:

$$\frac{W}{g}\frac{dV_w}{dH}(R/C)V = W(\Delta R/C) \quad (14:2)$$

Solving for the change in rate of climb in the standard engineering units, where the velocity gradient is expressed in mph per 1,000 ft:

$$\Delta R/C = .000067(R/C)V\frac{dV_w}{dH} \quad (14:3)$$

If an airplane is climbing at an airspeed of 200 mph in a vertical wind gradient of 5 mph per 1,000 ft, then the rate of climb will be increased by 7 per cent.

In the case of any vertical air currents, the air velocities encountered will be added algebraically to the normal rate of climb.

Several methods of climb performance reduction, all of which involve several assumptions and approximations, have been used, none of which is entirely satisfactory. The fact that climb is a dynamic state, since equilibrium conditions never actually obtain, introduces considerable complication in the academic analysis from which no practicable method has been deduced. Until such time as a more accurate and usable method is developed, the density altitude method in general use will be employed. The universal rate-of-climb-speed method is included for future reference.

Unless specifically requested otherwise, all airplane performance is calculated by aerodynamics, guaranteed, and determined from flight test based on N.A.C.A. standard atmospheric conditions. This means that the airplane configuration especially in regard to cowl flaps, coolant flaps or shutters, and other adjustable features, should be maintained in the state normally obtaining on a standard day. In case the atmospheric temperature is so greatly different from standard as to result in unsatisfactory engine operation due to improper engine temperatures, performance tests obviously must be run with the minimum configuration deviation to obtain satisfactory engine operation. In such a case, whether it be for level flight or climb performance, these changes must be evaluated and the final results adjusted to the desired standard conditions. Thus it will be necessary to make special tests evaluating speed or rate of climb versus cowl flap or shutter position over the maximum possible range and extrapolating the results if necessary. Data reduction methods are identical to those outlined here, and the only variable in the flight test runs will be the items under investigation. Plot the performance versus the position of the variables to determine the magnitude of performance variation.

14.2 Universal Rate-of-Climb-Speed Curve

At a given altitude and gross weight, climb conditions may be represented as in Figure 14:5.

If the propulsive efficiency in climb and the airplane characteristics are known, then the

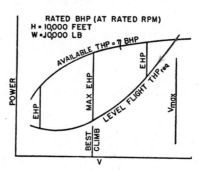

Fig. 14:5. Power available and power required curves

curves of Figure 14:5 may be drawn and the excess horsepower over that required for level flight (at some standard gross weight) is available for climbing by the simple physical relationship

$$R/C = \frac{(33,000)(EHP)}{W_s} \quad (14:4)$$

where

$$EHP = \eta(BHP) - THP_{req} \quad (14:5)$$

Combining these two equations gives the standard complete performance equation

$$R/C = \frac{33,000}{W_s}[\eta(BHP) - THP_{req}] \quad (14:6)$$

which reduces to the equation for level flight power, equation 12:1, when rate of climb is zero.

Equation 14:6 is written for standard gross weight where the expression for the thrust horsepower required is assumed to be given by equation 12:2 for level flight. By substitution and correction of the terms involving weight, the rate of climb at any gross weight will be:

$$R/C = \frac{33,000}{W_s}\left(\frac{W}{W_s}\right) \times$$

$$\left[\eta(BHP) - C_1\sigma V^3 - \frac{C_2}{\sigma V}\left(\frac{W}{W_s}\right)^2\right] \quad (14:7)$$

Multiplying the entire equation by $\sqrt{\sigma}(W_s/W)^{3/2}$ and reducing

$$R_w\sqrt{\sigma} = \frac{33,000}{W_s} \times$$

$$\left[\eta P_w\sqrt{\sigma} - C_1(V_w\sqrt{\sigma})^3 - \frac{C_2}{V_w\sqrt{\sigma}}\right] \quad (14:8)$$

where

$$R_w\sqrt{\sigma} = \frac{(R/C)\sqrt{\sigma}}{(W/W_s)^{1/2}} \quad (14:9)$$

$$P_w\sqrt{\sigma} = \frac{BHP\sqrt{\sigma}}{(W/W_s)^{3/2}} \quad (14:10)$$

$$V_w\sqrt{\sigma} = \frac{V\sqrt{\sigma}}{(W/W_s)^{1/2}} \quad (14:11)$$

$$N_w\sqrt{\sigma} = \frac{N\sqrt{\sigma}}{(W/W_s)^{1/2}} \quad (14:12)$$

(For C_1 and C_2, see section 12.2.)

Following the same reasoning as given in section 12.4, for constant values of $P_w\sqrt{\sigma}$ and $N_w\sqrt{\sigma}$, a plot of $R_w\sqrt{\sigma}$ versus $V_w\sqrt{\sigma}$ is rigorous and becomes independent of altitude and gross weight since propulsive efficiency, η, will not vary. The results are shown in Figure 14:6.

To obtain such a curve, a multitude of test points is required in order to arrive at lines of both constant $P_w\sqrt{\sigma}$ and $N_w\sqrt{\sigma}$ (whose values will vary for every test point) by a complicated procedure of cross plotting and fairing of the various parameters. Consequently, for the present, the method of correcting each point to standard conditions, as given in the next section, will be used during the present limitation of climb testing.

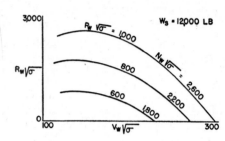

Fig. 14:6.   Universal rate-of-climb curves

14.3 Density Altitude Method

Data reduction involves first the determination of the rate of change of pressure altitude. For this purpose, an accurate plot of true pressure altitude versus time on a fairly large scale must be made and very careful attention given to fairing the curve. Since slopes are read at various altitudes along the curve any slight irregularities will be greatly magnified in the answer.

Having the actual pressure altitude rate of change, the actual, or tapeline, rate of climb is determined by the variation of the atmospheric temperature from standard. Equation 2:4 expresses the relation between pressure altitude increments at any temperature and tapeline distance and is directly applied here to find the actual rate of climb by:

$$R/C = \frac{dH_p}{dt} \times \frac{T}{T_s} \quad (14:13)$$

Having the actual rate of climb, further reduction to standard conditions presupposes constant atmospheric density, or density altitude. The next step is to obtain standard power versus density altitude for climbing conditions. This operation is independent of the above, and the methods have been outlined in Chapters 10 and 11. Above critical altitude, that is, for full throttle operation, use equation 11:4. Below critical altitude, if the engine manufacturer specifies constant power, the standard brake horsepower is already fixed and is extended to meet the standard full throttle power curve. If the engine manufacturer specifies a manifold pressure limitation, then the power chart power must be adjusted for the carburetor air temperature rise experienced under climbing conditions by equation 11:1. The resultant curve is again extended to meet the full throttle curve. Standard brake horsepower is now available at standard (density) altitude as shown in Figures 14:7 or 14:8.

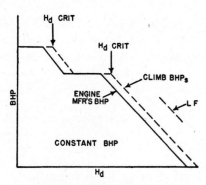

Fig. 14:7. Power available in climb for a typical engine rated at constant power

It is now necessary to correct the actual rate of climb to that which would obtain if the brake horsepower were standard. Note carefully that the density altitude at which the actual rate of climb was obtained and has been determined is known. However, when the actual power at the *density* altitude tested was converted to standard

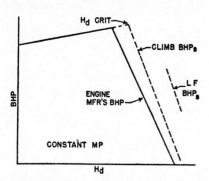

Fig. 14:8. Power available in climb for a typical engine rated at constant manifold pressure

brake horsepower, it was done by keeping the *pressure* altitude constant and correcting the temperature to standard conditions. This method is correct, but the standard power now obtains at a new density altitude (which expressed in terms of feet is the same as the test pressure altitude). Consequently, the standard and actual powers, since they are at different density altitudes, cannot be algebraically subtracted to obtain the desired brake horsepower increment.

It is necessary to plot standard brake horsepower versus density altitude for several points, and from a faired curve read standard brake horsepower at the density altitude for which the actual rate of climb has been obtained. Using numerical values, the following illustrates this principle.

Actual test values:

$$H_p = 10,000 \text{ ft}$$
$$t = 15°C$$
$$H_D = 12,300 \text{ ft}$$
$$R/C = 4,000 \text{ ft/min}$$
$$BHP = 1,500$$
$$t_c = 20°C$$

Calculated standard brake horsepower:

$$t_s = -5°C$$
$$t_{c_s} = 0°C$$
$$BHP_s = 1,668 \quad (n = 1.5)$$
$$H_D = 10,000 \text{ ft}$$

The 4,000-ft-per-minute rate of climb has been obtained at 12,300 ft density altitude using 1,500 brake horsepower. Holding constant airspeed,

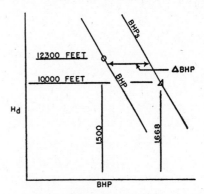

Fig. 14:9. Illustration of method for correcting power to standard conditions for climb

density altitude, and gross weight, it is desired to correct the test rate of climb for brake horsepower variation from standard. Therefore, the incremental power indicated in Figure 14:9 is desired. Hence it becomes necessary to determine the standard power at a series of altitudes to determine the faired curve shown. The standard power desired is then read from this curve at the desired 12,300 ft density altitude and

$$\Delta BHP = BHP_s - BHP \qquad (14:14)$$

The rate of climb increment for this power increment at the actual test gross weight is calculated, using equation 14:1, by

$$(\Delta R/C)_1 = \frac{33{,}000\eta\Delta\,\mathrm{BHP}}{W} \qquad (14{:}15)$$

where

η = propeller efficiency
= .8 (in lieu of specific data)

and

$$(R/C)_1 = (R/C) + (\Delta R/C)_1 \qquad (14{:}16)$$

Since for the case of saw-tooth climbs, the airspeed was held constant, or for the case of climb to ceiling, a selected airspeed schedule was maintained, no correction for speed is necessary. If the actual airspeed values vary too widely or are improper, the data should be discarded and the test repeated.

The foregoing reduction is complete for the case of a continuous climb from take-off made at standard gross weight, since the fuel consumption variation is natural. In the case of saw teeth, however, the variation of rate of climb with airspeed only is sought. Therefore, all data must be corrected to the same gross weight in order to eliminate the effect of this variable. Standard gross weight versus altitude should be approximated for a reasonable fuel consumption variation during a continuous climb in determining the standard gross weight to be used.

The total thrust horsepower required equals the sum of the parasite, induced, and excess for climb thrust horsepowers:

$$\mathrm{THP} = C_1\sigma V^3 + \frac{C_6 W^2}{\sigma V} + \frac{(R/C)_1 W}{33{,}000} \qquad (14{:}17)$$

Climb correction for weight is to be applied at constant power, density, and airspeed, so the propulsive efficiency will be constant, and equation 14:17 need not be converted to brake horsepower. Also the parasite thrust horsepower remains constant. Gross weight affects only the last two terms, and the conditions stated require that their sum, therefore, remain constant. If the gross weight increases, the induced power term increases, and the excess power term must be decreased by the same amount. Since the weight term in the excess power expression is increased the rate of climb must be reduced to fulfill the conditions stated.

Equating the induced and excess power terms

to a constant, then for small changes in weight and rate of climb, we may write

$$\frac{2\,C_6 W\Delta W}{V\sigma} + C_7[(R/C)_1\Delta W + W(\Delta R/C)_1] = 0$$
$$(14{:}18)$$

where

$C_6 = 1/3.01\,(ekb)^2$
$C_7 = 1/33{,}000$

If equation 14:18 is solved for $\Delta R/C$, its value will consist of the sum of two terms. For convenience, these two terms are written separately:

$$(\Delta R/C)_2 = -\ (R/C)_1\frac{\Delta W}{W} \qquad (14{:}19)$$

$$(\Delta R/C)_3 = -\ \frac{C_8\Delta W}{V\sigma} \qquad (14{:}20)$$

where

$$C_8 = 21{,}930/(ekb)^2$$

Thus for the known conditions of rate of climb, weight, and density for a given airplane, the complete effect of a weight change on rate of climb is calculated by the sum of equations 14:19 and 14:20. The final rate of climb reduced to standard conditions, that is, corrected for power and weight, is

$$(R/C)_s = (R/C) + (\Delta R/C)_1 + (\Delta R/C)_2$$
$$+ (\Delta R/C)_3 \qquad (14{:}21)$$

Final presentation of rate of climb performance reduced to standard conditions will appear as shown in Figure 14:10, where standard rate of

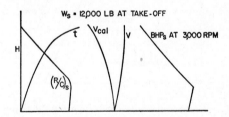

Fig. 14:10.   Presentation of climb performance reduced to standard conditions.

climb and standard brake horsepower are plotted against the density altitudes corresponding to the points selected from the original plot of pressure altitude versus time.

Both calibrated and true airspeeds for best climb are shown. The former when adjusted for position error is used by the pilot in making the climb, but its value is not affected by any particular airspeed system installation.

Note that the rate-of-climb curve at critical altitude is continuous. Such curves calculated by aerodynamics by assuming equilibrium conditions at each altitude are discontinuous and represent an instantaneous change in rate-of-climb deceleration at critical altitude. As flown, of course, such a condition cannot exist.

Above critical altitude, the rate-of-climb curve will approximate a straight line, but is usually slightly concave upwards as shown. Absolute ceiling is that altitude at which the rate of climb is zero, and service ceiling is specified as the altitude at which the rate of climb is 100 ft per minute.

The time to climb curve is simply a graphical integration of the rate of climb curve using increments not greater than 4,000 ft. A simple tabular method is illustrated in Table 11.

TABLE 11. TIME TO CLIMB CALCULATIONS

$\frac{H}{1,000}$	$(R/C)_s$	ΔH	Δt^*	Time
0	—	0	0	0
2	2,000	—	—	—
4	—	4,000	2.00	2.00
6	1,500	—	—	—
8	—	4,000	2.66	4.66
10	1,000	—	—	—
12	—	4,000	4.00	8.66

$* \Delta t = \Delta H/(R/C)_{\text{av}}.$

14.4 Data Reduction

First, it will be necessary to plot observed altitude versus time during climb in minutes using a large scale. Very careful attention must be given to the plotting and fairing of this curve because its slope at selected intervals will be measured, and any inconsistencies will become greatly exaggerated in the results. The remainder of the observed data should be plotted against observed altitude, which will be used in correlating all of the data.

In the case of saw-tooth climbs, gross weight should be estimated versus flight time in order to obtain the actual weight as tested for each saw tooth, since a weight correction must be made in this case only. (Climb to ceiling should be made with standard gross weight at take-off.)

The error in rate of change of pressure altitude as determined by the slope of the observed altitude time curve will be insignificant compared to the precise method of correcting all observed pressure altitudes for instrument and position errors, which is laborious. Error is involved only when instrument error and position error (or position error) plotted against altitude have an appreciable *slope*. This fact should be borne in mind, but its effect on the results will seldom be discernible and certainly will be insignificant compared to flight test inaccuracies. It is recommended that for climb tests an altimeter having the most desirable instrument calibration curve be selected from the altimeters available.

It is then convenient to select even altitude increments and record all of the observed data, which are correlated by observed altitude in Table 12, and perform the necessary operations. A detailed illustration of a typical set of data at one altitude is given.

Considering item 32, the exponent n is 0.5 for part throttle operation, or, the value determined in section 11.3 for full throttle. When the engine manufacturer's power curve below critical altitude specifies constant brake horsepower, this value is used as standard. If, however, constant manifold pressure is specified, the chart brake horsepower must be corrected to standard for the inherent carburetor air temperature rise using a value of 0.5 for the exponent n. The example in table 12 indicates that manifold pressure is specified and also that the pilot operated the throttle such that he maintained the scheduled value accurately.

Recording of the power plant flap and shutter positions should not be overlooked. Engine and oil temperature should also be noted and corrected to standard by the method specified by the contractor or engine manufacturer. The engine temperature limitations should not be exceeded for the climb performance determined.

14.5 Data Required

(a) *Gross weight* at take-off and landing.

(b) Sufficient data to determine the history of the gross weight throughout the flight.

(c) Frequent simultaneous readings of *time, pressure altitude, free air temperature, manifold pressure, carburetor air temperature, engine rpm,* and *airspeed.*

Time intervals should not be greater than one minute, preferably less. For modern pursuit airplanes, it is impossible for the pilot to obtain sufficient or satisfactory data, and some auto-

TABLE 12. RATE OF CLIMB DETERMINATION — DATA REDUCTION

1*	H_{p_r}	ft	28,000	Observed data: selected values.
2*	t	min	34.32	Observed data: from (1) vs. (2) at (1).
3	H_{p_m}	ft	28,050	H_{p_r} — lab. inst. cal. error.
4	H_p	ft	27,900	H_{p_m} — position error for (7) and (3).
5	dH_p/dt	ft/min	1,790	Slope of (1) vs. (2) at (1).
6*	V_r	mph	150	Observed data: at (1).
7	V_m	mph	147	V — lab. inst. cal. error.
8	V_{cal}	mph	142	V_m — position error for (7).
9	M	—	.323	Figure 8:1b for (8) and (4).
10	$M \sqrt{K}$	—	.28	Use K value for free air pickup used (.75 here).
11*	t_r	°C	−42	Observed data: at (1).
12	t_m	°C	−44.5	t_r — lab. inst. cal. error.
13	t	°C	−48	Figure 8:2a for (10) and (12).
14	V_c	mph	672	Figure 8:2a for (13).
15	V	mph	217	(9) × (14).
16	σ	—	.419	Figure 8:3c for (13) and (4).
17	H_D	ft	27,000	Figure 8:3c for (16).
18	t_s	°C	−40.2	Standard free air temperature from Figure 8:3c for (4).
19	T/T_s	—	.965	(13) + 273/(18) + 273.
20	R/C	ft/min	1,730	(5) × (19): eq. 14:13.
21*	RPM_r	1/min	3,010	Observed data: at (1).
22	RPM	1/min	3,000	RPM — lab. inst. cal. error.
23*	MP_r	in. Hg	41.5	Observed data: at (1).
24	MP	in. Hg	42	MP — lab. inst. cal. error.
25	BHP_{ch}	—	925	From power chart for (22), (24), and (4).
26*	t_{c_r}	°C	−37	Observed data: at (1).
27	t_c	°C	−35	t_{c_r} — lab. inst. cal. error.
28	$(T_s/T_c)^{.5}$	—	.990	(18) + 273/(27) + 273 and take square root.
29	BHP	—	916	(25) × (28): eq. 10:1.
	throttle	—	full	Note whether part or full throttle.
30	Δt_c	°C	13	(27) − (13).
31	t_{c_s}	°C	−27.2	(18) + (30).
32	$(T_c/T_{c_s})^n$	—	.951	$[(27) + 273]^n/[(31) + 273]^n$: n = 1.51 here.
33	BHP'_s	—	871	(29) × (32): eq. 11:4: plot (33) vs. (4).
34	BHP_s	—	904	Read from (33) vs. (4) at (17).
35	ΔBHP	—	−12	(34) − (29).
36*	W	lb	7,950	From curve of W vs. time for test.
37	η	—	.80	Use .8 unless better value known.
38	$(\Delta R/C)_1$	ft/min	−40	33,000 × (37) × (35)/(36): eq. 14:15.
39	$(R/C)_1$	ft/min	1,690	(20) + (38): eq. 14:16.
40	W_s	lb	8,500	Standard weight at (17).
41	ΔW	lb	550	(40) − (36).
42	$(\Delta R/C)_2$	ft/min	−117	− (39) × (41)/(36): eq. 14:19.
43	$(\Delta R/C)_3$	ft/min	−107	− (C_s) × (41)/(15) × (16): eq. 14:20.
44	$(R/C)_s$	ft/min	1,466	(39) + (42) + (43): eq. 14:21.

*Observed data recorded from the curve.

Notes: Plot standard rate of climb, item 44, against density altitude, item 17.
In item 43 the values of e = .93 and b = 38 ft are used in computing the constant C_s for the airplane in this example.
Table 12 outlines the data reduction for a set of saw-tooth climb data. For a climb to ceiling omit items 14 and 15 and 40 through 44. Standard rate of climb is then item 39.

matic means of recording data should be used. This method is preferable in large aircraft also, although manual data recording by several observers is possible. In the absence of proper instrumentation, various compromise methods of accumulating sufficient data are sometimes employed, including use of a barograph. At any rate, simultaneous readings of time and altitude are the most critical data.

In making saw teeth at least five different airspeeds should be investigated at each altitude. Stabilized conditions should be attained approximately 1,000 ft below and maintained to approximately 1,000 ft above each altitude investigated. In general three or more altitudes should be investigated, one at high altitude where the rate of climb is 400 to 500 ft per minute, one just below critical altitude, and one near the ground. For all part throttle operation, the power chart manifold pressure should be carefully followed.

Notes: The pressure lag in the static pressure lines of the airspeed head to which the altimeter is connected has been discussed in section 4.3. For this reason instruments in the static lines during climb tests should be held to an absolute minimum in order to reduce this lag error. Climb reduction is complicated enough without attempting to compensate for this altimeter lag, and the flight test accuracy at present does not warrant this extra labor. The rate-of-climb indicator and any miscellaneous duplicate instruments should be disconnected from the system.

Altimeter readings versus stop watch readings either manually or photographically recorded are preferred. Recording barographs offer no special advantages and should be avoided except for checking climb performance.

A complete check of the airspeed line system for leaks must be made before and after each flight.

CHAPTER 15

TAKE-OFF AND LANDING DISTANCES

15.1 Discussion

Like rate of climb, take-off is another dynamic flight condition and, consequently, the complicated accurate analysis is impractical. This complication is further aggravated by the fact that the take-off performance is largely dependent upon pilot technique. Different pilots will obtain widely different take-off performances with the same airplane, whereas the same pilot will find it extremely difficult to obtain the same results on successive tests.

Another factor involves the fact that the optimum take-off performance conditions of which the airplane is capable are dangerous, since flight at very low velocities, lower than possible without power, near the ground are required. Hence, take-off flight test results are more or less relative and optimum take-off performance is generally impractical.

Distance required to get off the ground or distance required to clear a 50-ft obstacle also may be required. Each requirement necessitates a different technique, a longer than optimum ground run being required to clear a 50-ft obstacle in the shortest over-all distance.

Partial deflection of the landing flaps will usually shorten take-off distances, but this variable is not always investigated.

Measurement of actual take-off tests also is difficult as a complete space time record of the airplane flight path is required, and the method and accuracy of reduction to standard conditions will be dependent upon the manner in which the data are obtained. Reduction methods outlined here assume the data available are the minimum data from which a reasonable reduction method may be derived.

A number of special instrumentation methods of take-off measurement are now becoming available. The best method is probably the photographic in which the camera is pivoted on a vertical axis to follow the airplane along its course. An azimuth scale in feet is included in the field of view, and time may be obtained either by an accurate timing of the single camera frames or by including the image of a stop watch on the film. Vertical distance may be scaled from a photograph or a grid of vertical distance may be superimposed on the negative. A space-time record of the actual flight path is required. A light in the airplane may be snapped at the instant of relieving the brakes for accurate correlation on the photographic record for the instant at which the take-off is begun.

The point at which the wheels last leave or first touch the ground should be spotted by ground observers. Then the camera may be swung back and a picture taken of the observer standing at this point.

Take-off tests should not be conducted in wind velocities exceeding about 10 per cent of the take-off speed.

15.2 Method for Ground Run Distance

For detailed theory of calculated take-off distance, see references 10 and 11. Reduction is based on fundamental simplifications from theory which have been corroborated by flight tests.

Required measurements are take-off distance, air density, wind velocity, engine operating conditions, ground speed at take-off, and gross weight. Since the reduction method is based on simple physics, ground velocities are used throughout. Take-off velocity determined from the airspeed indicator will not be very reliable because of inaccurate knowledge of the position error as well as other errors discussed in section 4.3.

Diehl's correction to ground-run distance for wind velocity is taken directly from his curve in reference 10, which may be expressed by the following equation:

$$S_0 = S \left(\frac{V_g + V_w}{V_g} \right)^{1.85} \qquad (15:1)$$

Here, S represents the measured take-off distance into a wind velocity, V_w, where the actual ground speed at take-off is V_g. Subscript $_0$ represents zero wind velocity conditions, so S_0 is the corresponding take-off distance in still air. Under these conditions the take-off velocity with respect to either the ground or the air is

$$V_0 = V_g + V_w \qquad (15:2)$$

It is then assumed that a plot of V/a, which is really time, versus V throughout the ground run, is a straight line. The area under this curve, up to the take-off velocity, is the ground-run distance. The method of reducing the take-off run to standard conditions is to determine $(V/a)_0$ and V_0, at take-off, for the zero wind conditions, correct them to their proper values under stand-

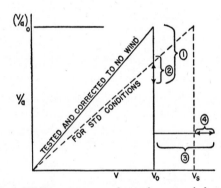

Area under solid line = test ground run for zero wind conditions
Area under dashed line = standard ground run
① for power   ③ for G.W.
② for G.W.   ④ for σ

Fig. 15:1. Time versus airspeed during ground run for actual run corrected to no wind and for standard conditions

ard conditions, and obtain the standard take-off distance as the area under the revised standard curve. Figure 15:1 is an illustration in which the power, density, and gross weight, as tested, are less than the standard values:

The figure shows that at a given velocity an increase in power will reduce V/a, and an increase in weight will increase V/a to arrive at the standard value for this velocity. This standard V/a now determines the slope of the line through the origin for standard conditions. The end point will be the take-off velocity under standard conditions, in which case a greater weight will increase it, and greater density will decrease it.

Considering only the take-off values of velocity and acceleration, the take-off ground run is given by

$$S_0 = \frac{1}{2} \left(\frac{V}{a} \right)_0 V_0$$

$$= \text{area of triangle (ft/sec units)} \qquad (15:3)$$

so the acceleration in engineering units is

$$a_0 = \frac{1.075 \, V_0^2}{S_0} \qquad (15:4)$$

and the effective net thrust producing this constant acceleration is calculated from $F = Ma$ by:

$$\Delta F_0 = \frac{W}{g} a_0 \qquad (15:5)$$

Now all of the necessary variables determined from flight test data corrected for wind velocity are known, and corrections to standard for the desired power, weight, and density may be determined. It is possible to calculate the actual gross propulsive thrust (reference 12) at 75 per cent of take-off speed (representing a good average condition) for the actual power, rpm, and density conditions of test. This calculation may be repeated using the desired standard conditions at the same airspeed; the detailed steps are given in section 15.6. The difference in these gross thrust values at the same airspeed will then be the additional net thrust increment under standard conditions, making the standard force available for acceleration:

$$\Delta F_s = \Delta F_0 + (F_s - F_0) \qquad (15:6)$$

The acceleration from equation 15:5 for standard conditions, including gross weight, becomes

$$a_s = \frac{g(\Delta F_s - \mu \Delta W)}{W_s} \qquad (15:7)$$

where

$\Delta W = W_s - W$

μ = rolling coefficient of friction (see references 10 and 21)

$\equiv$ .02 for hard surface

$\equiv$ .04 for firm turf

$\equiv$ .10 for soft turf

Using the same lift coefficient for take-off, the standard take-off velocity will be affected by gross weight and density

$$V_s{}^2 = V_0{}^2 \frac{W_s}{W} \frac{\sigma}{\sigma_s} \qquad (15{:}8)$$

Combining equations 15:4, 15:5, 15:7, and 15:8, the final equation for standard take-off distance becomes

$$S_s = S_0 \left(\frac{W_s}{W}\right)^2 \left(\frac{\Delta F_0}{\Delta F_s - \mu\Delta W}\right)\left(\frac{\sigma}{\sigma_s}\right) \qquad (15{:}9)$$

Take-off distance will vary roughly as the square of the gross weight, but for an accurate value the net accelerating force must be taken into consideration as evidenced by this term in the expression. Reasonable approximations may generally be made using an exponent of 2.2. If density alone is assumed to vary, take-off distance is a direct function of the ratio, but density will effect a change in power and hence net accelerating force.

15.3 Method for Air-Borne Distance

Required data are power conditions, horizontal distance to obstacle height, time, weight, density, and airspeed.

Correction to zero wind, which decreases the climb angle, simply increases the horizontal distance by the wind velocity times the time, the airspeed remaining constant:

$$S_0 = S + 1.467 \, V_w t \qquad (15{:}10)$$

The vectorial relationship between airspeed and rate of climb, which are not affected by wind velocity and ground velocity, are shown in Figure 15:2.

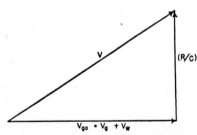

Fig. 15:2.   Climb flight path in still air

Reduction to standard power is made at constant equivalent airspeed and to standard gross weight and density at constant lift coefficient.

From the measurements of ground distance to

clear the given obstacle, usually 50 ft high, and time:

$$V_{g_0} = \frac{S_0}{1.467 \, t} \quad \text{and} \quad R/C = \frac{60 \, H}{t} \qquad (15{:}11)$$

from which

$$S_0 = \frac{88 \, V_{g_0} H}{(R/C)} \qquad (15{:}12)$$

so for standard conditions for the same obstacle height

$$S_s = S_0 \frac{V_{g_s}}{V_{g_0}} \frac{(R/C)}{(R/C)_s} \qquad (15{:}13)$$

The expression for rate of climb may be written in terms of excess horsepower:

$$R/C = \frac{33{,}000 \, \text{EHP}}{W}$$

$$= \frac{33{,}000}{W} [\eta\text{BHP} - (\eta\text{BHP} - \text{EHP})] \qquad (15{:}14)$$

The difference between thrust horsepower available and excess horsepower, the last term, is the thrust horsepower required for level flight. Since reduction is to be made at constant lift coefficient, and, therefore, constant drag coefficient, this thrust horsepower required will vary as the cube of the velocity and directly as the density:

$$\eta\text{BHP} - \text{EHP} = \frac{C_D{}'\sigma S V^3}{146{,}600} \qquad (15{:}15)$$

Writing the equation for lift coefficient for the actual and standard conditions:

$$C_L = \frac{391 \, W}{S\sigma V^2} = \frac{391 \, W_s}{S\sigma_s V_s{}^2} \qquad (15{:}16)$$

and dividing one by the other the variation of σV^3 may be found

$$\frac{\sigma_s V_s{}^3}{\sigma V^3} = \left(\frac{W_s}{W}\right)^{1.5} \left(\frac{\sigma}{\sigma_s}\right)^{.5} \qquad (15{:}17)$$

Equation 15:14 may now be written for standard brake horsepower, weight, and density:

$$(R/C)_s = \frac{33{,}000}{W_s} \times$$

$$\left[\eta\text{BHP}_s - (\eta\text{BHP} - \text{EHP})\left(\frac{W_s}{W}\right)^{1.5}\left(\frac{\sigma}{\sigma_s}\right)^{.5}\right] \qquad (15{:}18)$$

The ground speed may be corrected for the change in airspeed of equation 15:17 by

$$\frac{V_{g_s}}{V_{g_0}} = \frac{V_s}{V} = \left(\frac{W_s}{W}\right)^{.5} \left(\frac{\sigma}{\sigma_s}\right)^{.5} \quad (15:19)$$

If equations 15:19, 15:18, and 15:14 are substituted into equation 15:13, the complete expression for standard distance to clear the obstacle is

$$S_s = S_0 \left(\frac{W_s}{W}\right)^{1.5} \left(\frac{\sigma}{\sigma_s}\right)^{.5} \times$$

$$\left[\frac{EHP}{\eta BHP_s - (\eta BHP - EHP)(W_s/W)^{1.5}(\sigma/\sigma_s)^{.5}}\right]$$

$$(15:20)$$

Use $\eta = .80$ in lieu of better data.

The total standard distance to clear an obstacle is then the sum of the ground-run distance from section 15.2 and the air-borne distance from equation 15:20. The transition distance has been included in the air-borne phase of the take-off, which has assumed a straight flight path from the unsticking point to the top of the obstacle.

15.4 Alternate Obstacle Distance Method

If climb tests over an obstacle height are or can be made over a wide range of gross weights, and the results are corrected only for wind and density (sections 15.2 and 15.3), then the over-all take-off distance can be plotted as a function of power and wing loading. Having obtained an

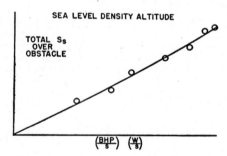

Fig. 15:3. Take-off distance over a 50-ft. obstacle versus universal parameter

empirical curve such as is shown in Figure 15:3, then standard distance for take-off and climb over the obstacle may be determined for any gross weight change and reasonable power variations.

15.5 Landing Roll Distance

Reduction of landing roll distance to standard is not of great importance. Wind velocity will affect the air-borne and ground-run distances in the same manner as for take-off. Since the glide angle is a function only of the ratio of the lift and drag coefficients, weight and density will not affect it. However, the contact velocity is affected by both weight and density. For landing results, the following equations may be used with sufficient accuracy:

$$S_s = S + 1.467 \, V_w t \text{ for glide over obstacle}$$

$$(15:21)$$

$$S_s = S \left(\frac{V_g + V_w}{V_g}\right)^{1.85} \frac{W_s}{W} \frac{\sigma}{\sigma_s} \text{ for landing roll}$$

$$(15:22)$$

15.6 Data Reduction

Sample calculations for take-off and climb distances over a 50-ft obstacle are given in Table 13.

15.7 Data Required

Ground and air distances.
Take-off ground speed.
Air time.
Power conditions.
Wind velocity.
Air temperature and pressure.
Gross weight.
Obstacle height.

Several practice take-offs should be made by the pilot to acquaint himself with the airplane characteristics and specific piloting technique for optimum results. The runway should be level, and the wind velocity should be no greater than 10 per cent of the take-off airspeed. Not less than three sets of take-off data for any given condition should be obtained, and the best results, neglecting distances appreciably different from the optimum values, should be averaged.

Wind velocity should be measured parallel to the take-off direction with an anemometer, and air temperature should be carefully measured in the shade.

Data from a number of tests should be averaged before reduction to standard, in order to avoid unnecessary labor of calculation.

TABLE 13. TAKE–OFF DISTANCE — DATA REDUCTION

			GROUND-RUN DISTANCE		
1*	S	ft	716	—	Observed data.
2*	V_g	mph	97	—	Observed data.
3*	V_w	mph	8	—	Observed data.
4	V_0	mph	105	—	(2) + (3): eq. 15:2.
5	S_0	ft	830	—	(1) $[(4)/(2)]^{1.85}$: eq. 15:1.
6	a_0	ft/sec^2	14.28	—	1.075 $(4)^2/(5)$: eq. 15:4.
7*	W	lb	6,950	—	Observed data.
8	ΔF_0	lb	3,080	—	$(7) \times (6)/g$: eq. 15:5.
9*	H_p	ft	980	—	Observed data.
10*	t	°C	20	—	Observed data.
11	σ	—	.95	—	Figure 8:3a for (9) and (10).
12*	RPM	1/min	3,050	—	Observed data.
13*	MP	in. Hg	51	—	Observed data.
14	BHP_{ch}	—	1,211	—	From engine power chart.
15*	t_c	°C	22	—	Observed data.
16	BHP	—	1,208	—	$(14) [(10) + 273]^{.5}/[(15) + 273]^{.5}$: eq. 10:1.
17	BHP_s	—	—	1,250	Standard power rating.
18	RPM_s	1/min	—	3,000	Standard rpm.
19	σ_s	—	—	1.0	Standard sea level density ratio.
20	N	1/min	1,368	1,345	RPM/2.23.
21	C_p	—	.120	.118	Items 21–31 by Hamilton Standard Method.
22	P_{AF}	—	.81	.81	Ref. 12 or other equivalent method.
23	P_h	—	.99	.99	—
24	C_B	—	.70	.70	—
25	$C'p$	—	.0675	.066	—
26	$(C_t/C_P)_{900}$	—	1.32	1.35	—
27	$\pi ND/60$	ft/sec	830	816	—
28	S_t	—	1.0	1.0	—
29	S_B	—	1.01	1.01	—
30	F_{st}	lb	3,360	3,610	—
31	$.75 \times 88 V_0/ND$	—	.437	.445	J at .75 V_0.
32	F/F_{st}	—	.92	.91	—
33	F_0	lb	3,100	—	—
34	F_s	lb	—	3,280	—
35	$F_s - F_0$	lb	180	—	(34) − (33).
36	ΔF_s	lb	3,260	—	(8) + (35).
37	W_s	lb	7,100	—	Standard weight.
38	ΔW	lb	150	—	(37) − (7).
39	$\mu\Delta W$	lb	3	—	$.02 \times (38)$ for hard surfaces.
40	S_s	ft	779	—	Eq. 15:9.
			AIR-BORNE DISTANCE		
41*	H	ft	50	—	Observed data: obstacle height.
42*	t	sec	3	—	Observed data: time from take-off to obstacle.
43*	S	ft	650	—	Observed data.
44	S_0	ft	685	—	(43) + 1.467 (3)(42): eq. 15:10.
45	R/C	ft/min	1,000	—	60 (41)/(42): eq. 15:11.
46	EHP	—	210	—	(7)(45)/33,000: eq. 15:14.
47	ηBHP	—	966	—	.8 (16).
48	ηBHP_s	—	1,000	—	.8 (17).
49	$\left(\dfrac{W_s}{W}\right)^{1.5}\left(\dfrac{\sigma}{\sigma_s}\right)^{.5}$		1.008		$[(37)/(7)]^{1.5} (11)^{.5}$.
50	S_s	ft	628	—	Eq. 15:20.
			TOTAL DISTANCE		
51	S_s	ft	1,407	—	(40) + (50).

*Flight test data required.

CHAPTER 16

RANGE AND ENDURANCE

16.1 Discussion

A great many variables enter into the determination of range, and all of them are varying through a long flight. Economical range is affected by altitude, gross weight, power, rpm, speed, and specific fuel consumption. Fuel consumption and propulsive efficiency cause most of the complication in range determination.

By means of speed-power polars, full throttle engine-airplane-propeller power curves, and engine specific fuel consumption curves over the proper ranges, the theory of determination of range or endurance for any condition is very simple. However, considerable labor is involved because cross plots of several of the variables are required in order to determine the optimum or desired values.

The basic method as outlined here can be extended to cover any specified range or endurance condition.

16.2 Method

The universal or conventional speed-power polar (sections 13.2 and 13.3) specifies completely the relationships between gross weight, altitude, speed, power, and rpm insofar as the airplane is concerned. When the fuel consumption of the engine is determined for these operating conditions, the endurance may be determined, or when combined with the speed variable, the range may be obtained. As before, the engine characteristics may be divorced from the airplane-propeller characteristics insofar as the engine's ability or efficiency in producing the required power is concerned. Figures 16:1 and 16:2 represent these engine characteristics, which when combined with the speed-power polars, will be sufficient to determine any level flight performance desired.

This standard level flight power curve is obtained from full throttle level flight test points at each rpm in the same manner as indicated in sec-

tion 11.2. Use may be made of engine power curves discussed in Chapter 11 in reducing flight test time. That is, if one standard full throttle power versus altitude curve is obtained for each

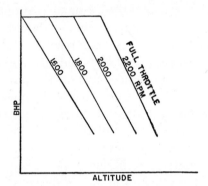
Fig. 16:1. Power available

of two rpm's in the cruising range, then at several altitudes a cross plot of standard power versus rpm (using the previously determined rated rpm curve as extra data), may be faired using the engine power curve data as a guide. These curves

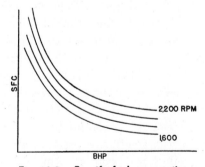
Fig. 16:2. Specific fuel consumption

will supply interpolated points so that all of the standard full throttle rpm lines may be determined as shown in Figure 16:1. Such curves should be obtained for the mixture setting desired.

Curves of specific fuel consumption variation with power and rpm should be obtained from flight test by measuring the rate of fuel flow under the various engine operating conditions. Variation of altitude has practically no effect on specific

83

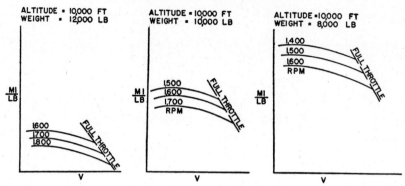

Fig. 16:3.   Variation of miles per pound of fuel with true airspeed, engine rpm, and gross
weight at constant altitude

fuel consumption. Care should be taken to specify the mixture setting and the blower ratio for which these curves are obtained. Engine manufacturer's specific fuel consumption curves should be used as a guide in fairing test data results. All fuel consumption terms should be based on weight of fuel rather than volume inasmuch as the power available from the fuel is a function of the mass of fuel, and its specific gravity varies with its temperature.

If the speed-power polars at several low rpm values are obtained (section 13.3) and combined with the engine specific fuel consumption curves, then miles per pound of fuel, a measure of range for the particular instantaneous conditions, may be plotted against speed for constant rpm parameters at any altitude and gross weight, as illustrated in Figure 16:3.

In fairing speed-power curves, it is sometimes helpful to calculate the propulsive efficiencies for the test points and plot thrust horsepower required against speed. Since this plot is independent of rpm, all the tests points should fall on one curve. This faired curve and the relation of the various test points to it will help in judicious fairing of the brake horsepower curves. If the gross weight variation for the data is obtained, the correction, equation 13:1, should be applied as this variable has a large effect on speed values for the comparatively low speed at which economical range occurs.

For any desired conditions and values obtained from the polars and specific fuel consumption curves, the calculations required are simply

$$\text{lb/hr} = (\text{BHP})(\text{SFC}) \qquad (16:1)$$

$$\text{mi/lb} = \frac{V}{\text{lb/hr}} = \frac{V}{(\text{BHP})(\text{SFC})} \qquad (16:2)$$

From these curves the final plot of mi/lb or

hr/lb against gross weight may be made for any specified operating conditions from which the total range or endurance may be obtained as the

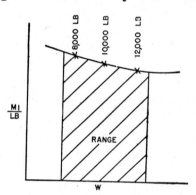

Fig. 16:4.   Curve for range determination

area under the curves, as shown in Figures 16:4 and 16:5.

These curves may have been drawn for maximum range, in which case the miles per pound

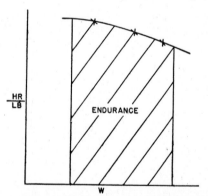

Fig. 16:5.   Curve for endurance determination

values would have been taken at the peak values from the miles per pound versus V curves. Usually, for maximum range conditions pounds of fuel per mile will plot as a straight line against gross weight, in which case range may be calculated from it as in Figure 16:6.

$$\text{Range} = \frac{2.303}{b} \log_{10} \frac{C_1}{C_2} \qquad (16\!:\!3)$$

where $b = dC/dW$ = slope of curve
       C_1 = lb/mi at W_1
       C_2 = lb/mi at W_2

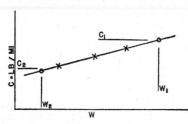

Fig. 16:6.   Pounds of fuel per mile versus gross weight

In the process of obtaining the maximum range, all of the required flight conditions also are available. It is possible to plot the curves illustrated in Figures 16:7 and 16:8 for use by the pilot as a

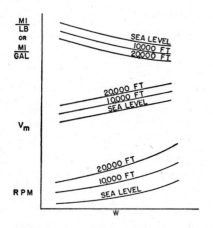

Fig. 16:7.   Optimum range flight conditions versus gross weight

guide in flying the airplane at its optimum conditions throughout the flight. Note that manifold pressure is not considered as an operating condi-

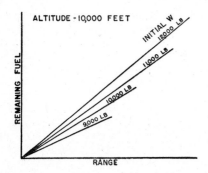

Fig. 16:8.   Curves for determining range available with remaining fuel

tion, since the speed, altitude, rpm, and gross weight define the power that is required. The manifold pressure required to produce this power

will automatically be utilized when the pilot adjusts the throttle, at the governing rpm, to attain the proper airspeed.

In general, economical range will be found at low rpm but at full throttle (minimum throttling losses), which means high brake mean effective pressure. Range is not seriously affected by altitude, but often the lowest supercharging operation in the vicinity of its critical altitude is best. The speed for maximum range will occur at a slightly higher speed than that for minimum drag, but specifically the engine fuel consumption and propulsive efficiencies of the propeller alter the theoretical minimum drag operating conditions.

Effect of head or tail winds may easily be determined from a revision of the miles per pound of fuel versus speed curves for any wind velocity. Values of miles per pound are simply redetermined on the basis of the shift in ground speed caused by the wind and replotted against airspeed. The resultant range and new optimum airspeeds are then determined from these new basic curves in the same manner as before.

Effective bombing radius is easily found for any disposable load and fuel capacity based on a

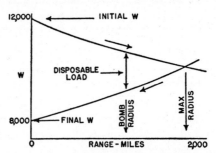

Fig. 16:9.   Curves for determining weight of fuel required for various missions

simple integration of either the miles per pound or pounds per mile versus gross weight curve. Calculate range versus gross weight variation from the initial gross weight and also from the weight empty, or final gross weight, and plot the curves shown in Figure 16:9.

Any desired operation performance is thus available from the fundamental basic curves of miles per pound of fuel versus airspeed for various rpm parameters, which are obtained by combining the speed-power polars with the specific fuel consumption curves. The importance of determining these fundamental curves from flight testing over a sufficiently wide range of conditions is obvious, as the analysis of these basic curves will yield any results desired. From these fundamental concepts any desired range or endurance operation may be completely derived and presented in any desired manner.

Many possible limitations must be carefully observed. For instance, at low values of rpm required for economical range at low altitudes, the generator may cut out. Also, if maximum cruising brake mean effective pressure rating is exceeded, the engine may not be operated with lean mixture settings. High brake mean effective pressures occurring at low rpm's and altitudes with high powers may not be permitted for continuous operation. Naturally, full throttle may

TABLE 14.   BASIC RANGE DATA COMPUTATIONS
AT ONE ALTITUDE

1	2	3	4	5	6	7	8
RPM	N	W	V	BHP	SFC	lb/hr	mi/lb
x	x	x	x	x	x	x	x
			x	x	x	x	x
			x	x	x	x	x
			x	x	x	x	x
		x	x	x	x	x	x
(REPEAT FOR SEVERAL SPEEDS.)							
			x	x	x	x	x
		x	x	x	x	x	x
(REPEAT FOR SEVERAL SPEEDS.)							
			x	x	x	x	x
x	x	x	x	x	x	x	x
(REPEAT ABOVE FOR EACH RPM.)							

(1) Select engine rpm's over range desired.
(2) Propeller $N = $ (RPM)(GR).
(3) At least three gross weights for each rpm.
(4) Select at least four values over the range desired from speed-power polar.
(5) Read brake horsepower values for (4).
(6) From specific fuel consumption curves for brake horsepower and rpm values.
(7) Equation 16:1.
(8) Equation 16:2.

not be exceeded, and this limitation should be observed when making calculations by referring to the airplane-engine-propeller full-throttle power curves mentioned earlier. Careful attention should be paid to the mixture settings at which the powers and fuel consumption curves were obtained. Hand leaning will result in more

economical operation than automatic lean carburetor mixture settings.

The application of range data is very extensive and the particular problems of a given airplane must be left to the judgment of the data analysis engineer.

16.3 Data Reduction

Table 14 is suggested for determination of the basic miles per pound of fuel versus true airspeed curves from the speed-power polars and specific fuel consumption curves. Each table represents one altitude. Bear in mind that at higher altitudes it may be possible to obtain greater range with a high blower ratio than with a low blower ratio. The purpose of complete tabular calculations is to determine the effects of all such variables, which will be revealed in the plotted results.

16.4 Data Required

The following data are required in addition to that required for determination of speed-power polars (section 13.3).

Fuel flow from flowmeter:
  Rate of fuel flow (pounds per hour).
Fuel flow from flow tanks:
  Volume of fuel passed (gallons).
  Corresponding time (seconds).
  Fuel temperature or hydrometer reading in order to determine pounds per hour. Curve of specific gravity of the fuel versus temperature is required unless hydrometer reading is taken.
Mixture setting.
Throttle position.
Blower ratio.

Notes: The range of tests required depends upon the extent of the desired results. On any standard airplane a comprehensive speed-power polar should be obtained, which means that a wide range of engine speeds should be covered, and fuel flow readings should be taken throughout the tests.

Unstable atmospheric conditions, especially vertical air currents, will greatly affect test results, especially range. Tests should be made in smooth air away from cloud formations and over a large body of water if possible.

Any set of runs should be made at constant rpm, changing speed by changing throttle position. Runs should be repeated at selected altitudes both at high and at low gross weights. Constant rpm runs are desired as this is the parameter used in fairing all speed power polars.

No positive displacement flowmeters have as yet proven satisfactory, and they should be avoided. Accurate kinetic-type flowmeters are available and are preferred. Fuel flow tanks must be used as an alternate method of measuring fuel consumption.

CHAPTER 17

STABILITY AND CONTROL

17.1 Introduction

17.11 General

The stability characteristics of a given airplane about each of its three axes may vary with gross weight, center of gravity location, configuration changes, flight attitude, rate of change of attitude, power conditions, and Reynolds or Mach number variations. Stability analysis is extremely complicated and highly theoretical, and practical methods of complete analysis are not available. Consequently, when the subject arises, the confusion that is usually encountered reveals the fact that there are no concrete definitions, specifications, or method of stability determination, especially concerning its degree of acceptability. Methods outlined here represent only an approach to some of the problems.

In general, the airplane characteristics about its three individual axes may be broken down into two classifications. For practical purposes and relatively small variations, longitudinal stability, revolving about the lateral spanwise axis, may be isolated from the interdependent lateral and directional characteristics about the other two axes. At present, the former tends to be more troublesome and receives more attention than the latter because center of gravity location and compressibility primarily affect longitudinal stability. Fortunately, changes in either of these two general categories will not seriously affect the other.

17.12 Types of Stability and Motion

First, stability may be appraised for the case of fixed or locked controls or for the case of *free* controls. In general, better stability results from fixed controls, so if the characteristics for free control are satisfactory, there need be little concern for the " stick fixed " case. However, by introducing mechanical forces with weights or springs, the reverse situation is possible.

Second, for each of these cases, there will be two categories of oscillations to be considered. One type of oscillation arising from instantaneous displacement of the control surface will be of very *short period*, a second or considerably less, and generally is very highly damped. Usually this type of oscillation is not critical and seldom causes concern. In reality this phenomenon involves variations of angle of attack at essentially constant speeds. If not damped, this type of instability could induce flutter, which is a type of forced oscillation.

A second type of oscillation characterized by a *long period*, of the order of one minute, may also be found. This long period oscillation involves variation of speed at an essentially constant angle of attack and has no noticeable correlation with the ability of a pilot to fly the airplane efficiently. The degree of damping of this motion is not critical as a pilot normally would never notice this oscillation unless he consciously set out to detect it.

Stability for stick fixed controls is desired so that the pilot may operate the airplane with the minimum amount of continuous attention, although this is not as important for fighter aircraft as for transports or bombers. Thus, it is most important under cruising or other conditions of flight, where a relatively long period of operation is encountered, in order to reduce pilot fatigue or objectionable flight characteristics. Free control stability is desirable from the standpoint of emergency conditions. That is, it is desirable that the airplane maintain a given set of flight conditions for reasonably long periods of time without any pilot influence.

Finally, stability may be studied in two parts: *static* stability and *dynamic* stability. A body has static stability when, after an initial displacement, it tends to return towards its initial equilibrium condition. When it will return to its original equilibrium condition depends upon the damping of the oscillation initiated. The body has dynamic stability when the motion is damped so that it does return to the original condition. It therefore follows that a body must possess static stability if it is to have dynamic stability, but the converse is not true.

Various degrees of dynamic longitudinal stability are illustrated in Figure 17:1 showing airspeed or displacement versus time, wherein the variation is caused by longitudinal oscillations,

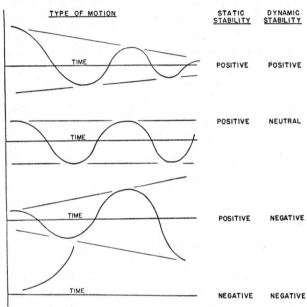

Fig. 17:1. Various types of longitudinal phugoids

that is, as the attitude of the airplane in pitch alternately increases and decreases. These phugoids are the long period oscillations and may be investigated for fixed or free controls after an initial displacement.

17.13 Flight Conditions

There are many different conditions of flight, and under each condition the airplane may behave differently. The most representative conditions of operation which must be satisfactory, those which require investigation, are as follows:

(a) Landing: flaps and gear down, power off, approach speed trim.

(b) Approach: flaps and gear down, 50 per cent power, approach speed trim.

(c) Climb: flaps for optimum climb, gear up, high power, cowl flaps set for cooling, best climb speed trim.

(d) Cruise: flaps and gear up, cruise power, level flight trim.

(e) High speed: flaps and gear up, maximum power, level flight trim.

(f) Dive: dive flaps down, gear up, allowable engine speed, high speed level flight trim.

(g) Stall: flaps and gear up, power off, approach speed trim.

(h) Stall: various flap positions, gear down, power off, climb trim.

At each of these conditions, it will be necessary to investigate specified ranges of gross weights, center of gravity locations, speeds, and, in some cases, altitudes.

17.14 Requirements

Broadly speaking, there are two contradictory stability and control requirements. One requires inherent free control stability such that the airplane will, under specified conditions, fly itself and resist any changes due to external or miscellaneous forces or displacements. The other requires that the pilot be able to manipulate the airplane easily and conveniently at will. Obviously, the first requirement could easily be satisfied by making the airplane very stable or "stiff," in which case the pilot would have as much ability to maneuver and control it as an engineer has over a locomotive. Therefore, any chosen requirements must be some compromise of these two, depending upon the type of aircraft and its purpose.

For a fighter airplane, the free control stability should be only slightly positive so that the pilot may easily maneuver the airplane, while for a transport greater free control stability and less maneuverability are desired. Actual requirement specification is a function of the purpose for which the airplane is to be used plus pilot opinion or preference concerning the desirable compromise. Therefore, every attempt should be made to obtain specific requirements insofar as possible from the customer regarding the purpose of the airplane and his preferences. These requirements, however, should not attempt to encompass too broad a scope as it is impossible to obtain desired characteristics under many different conditions in one airplane.

Army requirements may be found in reference 22 and Army-Navy procedures in reference 23. From the preceding discussion, it is realized that the permutations and combinations of possible test conditions are infinite, and considerable judgment must be used in investigating the stability and flight characteristics of an airplane. Reference 24 gives R. R. Gilruth's N.A.C.A. requirements, which were published prior to his collaboration with the Army in formulating reference 22.

Spiral stability is usually divergent and is most violent at high lift coefficients. However, this motion is easily controlled, and changes to effect spiral stability will conflict with other more important flying characteristics. Therefore, spiral stability is ruled out of the picture.

Friction in the control system is another matter which must be given careful consideration. Friction in the system tends to defeat free control stability by resisting any tendencies present to neutralize or center the controls. For a fighter, elevator control friction in excess of 2 lb or aileron friction in excess of 1 lb cannot be tolerated. In the case of a bomber or transport 10 lb and 6 lb respectively represent practical limits. Friction may act favorably to dampen free control dynamic oscillations or unfavorably to induce flutter on a free surface if it acts out of phase.

17.15 Types of Control Surfaces

There are three types of tabs operating at the trailing edge of the movable control surfaces: trim, balancing, and servo tabs.

Figure 17:2 shows a trim tab adjustable by the pilot. It is adjusted relative to the movable surface by an irreversible operating mechanism

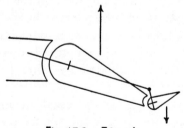

Fig. 17:2. Trim tab

passing through the control surface hinge line. This tab, by means of a small aerodynamic force on it, changes the free float angle of the control surface, which in turn creates a large force, the control surface hinge moment being zero. If trim variation during flight is small, a fixed extension of sheet metal may be attached to the trailing edge of the surface, adjustable only on the ground.

Figure 17:3 is a balancing tab operated by a linkage to the fixed surface. This tab reduces the control forces required to deflect the control surface. By various linkage lengths any degree of balancing action may be achieved, or a tab having

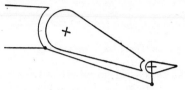

Fig. 17:3. Balancing tab

reverse action, an antibalance tab, may be designed to "heavy" control surfaces. Spring tabs, which are balancing tabs operated on a force ratio rather than a deflection ratio, may be employed with varying results.

A servo tab is similar to Figure 17:2 except that the pilot operates the tab with his controls and has no direct linkage to the control surface itself. Servo tabs find application on very large airplanes where the forces to operate the control surface directly may be too great.

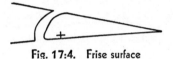

Fig. 17:4. Frise surface

Many types of control surfaces are in use. The Frise type of control surface, Figure 17:4, has been used extensively on ailerons because of its more favorable yaw characteristics as a result of differential aileron displacement.

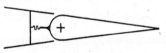

Fig. 17:5. Pressure balance

Pressure balanced control surfaces, Figure 17:5, are used to reduce the control forces. When the surface is deflected, the air pressures in the sealed balance act to reduce the applied control forces. Varying the percentage of balance, leakage, or

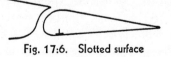

Fig. 17:6. Slotted surface

skin surface angles ahead of the control surface will produce large changes in the action of this control surface. Chordwise gap location is very important.

Hydraulically and pneumatically boosted control surfaces have been used successfully by applying large forces to help the pilot deflect the control surfaces.

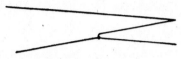

Fig. 17:7.   Split surface

Various types of control surfaces, such as Fowler, slotted, plain, split, and deflector-plate, are chosen for their particular aerodynamic characteristics.

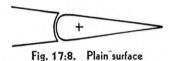

Fig. 17:8.   Plain surface

The shape of the control surface also is an important variable. Bulged surfaces tend to float more into the wind and reduce control forces. Aerodynamic balance area ahead of the hinge

Fig. 17:9.   Deflector-plate

line is commonly used to reduce control forces for deflected surfaces. Wedge and beveled trailing edges as well as trailing edge cords also tend to act in the same manner as trim tabs considered

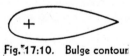

Fig. 17:10.   Bulge contour

acting in the windward direction when deflected.

These various types of surfaces are merely enumerated here to suggest the large field of possibilities available for changing control surface

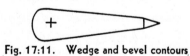

Fig. 17:11.   Wedge and bevel contours

characteristics. Concerning the fixed airfoils, their sections as to thickness, camber, section, and type may be widely varied as well as the leading edge shapes. Areas and aspect ratio may also be increased to improve stability.

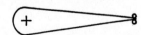

Fig. 17:12.   Cord or bead trailing edge

17.16 Method of Approach

Specific procedures for stability and control investigations cannot be outlined completely because each individual airplane will have its own characteristics and problems. A new airplane is investigated qualitatively by the pilot to form a general opinion of its acceptability. If required, some quantitative data must be taken. This process usually uncovers certain deficiencies and indicates a course of investigation and research to be pursued.

During all early phases of testing, it is advisable to deal only with observed data to indicate trends and general results, as correction and reduction of data does not alter its significance. Toward the culmination of a program, it may be preferable to correct all data to true values, although reduction to standard conditions would be of no consequence.

Again the desirability of an airspeed head having no position error may be reiterated. During accelerated flight considerable changes in lift coefficient result. Although position error is a function of lift coefficient, it is normally plotted as a function of measured airspeed for more convenient use. This correction may be appreciable, requiring more work in data reduction as well as reducing the accuracy of the results (section 5.5).

Wind tunnel tests afford very valuable information on certain problems, and, where possible, their use should not be overlooked. For example, it would be very dangerous to spin test an airplane with bad recovery characteristics for the effect of various changes. Modifications should be tested on a spin tunnel model and the most promising configuration incorporated in the flight test airplane. Other benefits, such as changes in airfoil section, shape, and scoop entrances, may be more profitably exploited by wind tunnel tests first.

Caution should be exercised in interpreting stability results from wind tunnel tests. Model tests are often made by varying the attitude of the body, but keeping the airspeed constant. This serves to vary the lift coefficient by varying the lift, while in flight the lift must always equal the weight in level flight. In case mass forces are introduced, the wind tunnel results will lead to erroneous conclusions. Figure 17:13 shows how the ratio of weight to aerodynamic force in the wind tunnel will be constant at constant airspeed, while in flight it varies greatly. Such a situation would lead to greater apparent stick free than stick fixed static stability from wind tunnel results, while the reverse may be true in flight.

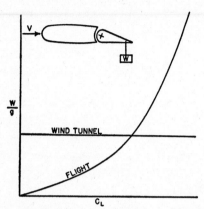

Fig. 17:13. Variation of ratio of weight to aerodynamic forces in wind tunnel tests at constant tunnel speed and in free flight

17.2 Preliminary Stability and Control Check

The following itemized tests are conducted in the preliminary phases of flight testing in order to obtain as far as possible a complete but general impression of the suitability of the airplane from the standpoint of stability and handling qualities. For first flights, ballast to 25 per cent mean aerodynamic chord center of gravity location.

(a) Stalls at safe altitude: all combinations of gear up and down and flaps up and down; also, various cowl flaps, shutter, cabin hatch, or other miscellaneous changes; note stall warning and speeds, stalling characteristics, control at stall, and loss of altitude during recovery. Stall warning is essential. If not a natural phenomenon, an aerodynamic or mechanical warning device must be incorporated.

(b) Longitudinal phugoids: trim the airplane for climb, cruising, high speed, and approach conditions; reduce its speed 20 mph and release the stick, noting oscillation characteristics. Maintain heading with rudder.

(c) Directional phugoids: same conditions as (b); displace and release the rudder at small and large deflections, keeping the wings level with the stick, and note the directional oscillation characteristics.

(d) Lateral phugoids: roll the airplane 15 to 20 degrees and release the stick, using the rudder and elevator trim tab to maintain linear flight if possible, and note the results.

(e) S-turns, rudder only: make steady turns up to a 30-degree bank using rudder only and make reverse turns for both slow and rapid rudder applications; use fore and aft pressure on the stick if necessary; note the effect of the rudder in initiating and maintaining turns; if it is unsatisfactory, try returning the rudder to neutral after obtaining a steady turn.

(f) S-turns, stick only: repeat (e), using the stick only for slow and rapid aileron application.

(g) Co-ordination: execute various turns and maneuvers to evaluate co-ordination of all controls and their relative forces.

(h) Trim tab effectiveness: investigate the adequacy of the trim tab by trimming at approach, climb, level flight speed range, and dive conditions to see if the tab has adequate range; at cruising speed vary the trim tab throughout its range and note its effectiveness by control forces produced.

(i) Short period oscillations: check all controls by instantaneous and violent displacements; oscillations of the control should disappear in one or two cycles.

(j) Static stability: check the displacement of each control from trimmed flight both ways to see that the force gradients with respect to control deflections and control travel are in the right direction and of reasonable magnitudes.

(k) Fin stall: check for fin stall or rudder reversal by severe side slips at moderate speeds.

(l) Ground handling: check taxiing, ground handling, cross-wind effects, and elevator power for stall attitude at about three quarters of take-off speed.

(m) Accelerated flight: dive the airplane at various speeds and pull out at various accelerations to note the stick force gradients and accelerated stall characteristics. Check steady accelerated turns and high-speed stalls.

These tests should form the basis for a general impression of the airplane's flying characteristics and indicate any deficiencies requiring further investigation. If additional testing is necessary, a carefully organized program outlining specific objectives should be formulated before further testing is undertaken. Remember that possible programs are infinite and that changes to correct one difficulty may introduce other undesirable effects.

17.3 Longitudinal Static Stability in Linear Flight

17.31 Purpose

If static stability under both linear and accelerated flight conditions is satisfactory, then positive dynamic stability will generally result, although phugoids should be rechecked at the conclusion of the program. Measurement of control forces and positions are required, for which reliable instrumentation is necessary. Forces should be measured at the points of application, but control surface positions must be measured at the control surfaces because of deflections in the control systems.

Observed flight data are sufficient for preliminary analysis to indicate general magnitudes and trends.

17.32 Stick Fixed Static Stability

Trim the airplane for the given flight condition and loading, and measure the elevator angle versus speed for stabilized conditions at constant power.

The curve for various speeds may be determined from a continuous record during a slow rate of change of airspeed or by taking data at a number of stabilized speeds. In general, both methods will give the same results, but for the high speeds a continuous record lasting about two minutes is preferred, while at the slower speeds spot check points are desirable. The same is true for stick free static stability tests.

It is advisable for analytical purposes to obtain records from a recording accelerometer. Near trim speed the stick forces are so light that the effects of control system friction will make the exact trim speed somewhat indefinite, but it should be determined by the complete faired curve result. Wings should be kept level, which means that at the slower airspeeds and high powers some yaw will be induced if roll is to be prevented.

A negative slope of this curve throughout its range, that is, from stall to high speed, is indicative of positive stick fixed static stability: the steeper the slope the greater the stability. Assume the airplane to be trimmed for the elevator position as shown by point a in Figure 17:14. If the elevator position remains fixed, and the speed is inadvertently reduced to that at point b, then the elevator is set for nose down with respect to this

new speed. The result is that the nose will drop, and the speed will increase again until point a is regained. Conversely, if the speed were increased the same reasoning applies, and the speed will be reduced to the trim speed again. Obviously, if the slope is positive, there is no restoring tendency,

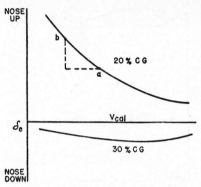

Fig. 17:14.   Elevator deflection versus calibration airspeed

and the stability will be negative. A small stick travel of about 4 in. for trim throughout the speed range is desirable on a fighter, while for other aircraft a larger travel may be preferred.

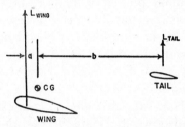

Fig. 17:15.   Relation of lift forces to center of gravity

The reason for the adverse effect of rearward center of gravity shift is illustrated in Figure 17:15 showing the wing and tail loads and their moment arms about the center of gravity. Moving the center of gravity aft increases the de-

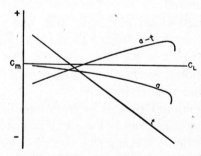

Fig. 17:16.   Pitching moment coefficient versus lift coefficient for airplane less tail, tail alone, and complete airplane

stabilizing moment caused by the wings and decreases the restoring tail moment. Typical pitching moment coefficients versus lift coefficient are illustrated in Figure 17:16 showing the curves for airplane less tail, tail alone, and the complete airplane as the sum of the two. Moving the center of gravity aft rotates the first two curves about the zero lift coefficient in a destabilizing manner such that the desirable negative slope for the complete airplane is reduced.

17.33 Stick Free Static Stability

Stick free static stability for a given linear flight condition is obtained from a curve of stick force versus airspeed, varying the speed from that for trim using constant power as shown in Figure 17:17.

Trim is represented by the speed for zero stick force. Should the speed be changed, but the stick left free, the push or pull forces to maintain the

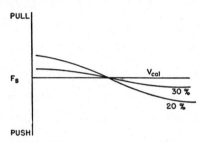

Fig. 17:17.   Elevator stick force versus airspeed

new speed are not applied and the tendeney to regain the trim speed results automatically. Thus a negative slope again indicates positive stability. Since the variation of stick force with speed is not linear it is more advantageous to plot F_s/q versus C_L for actual analysis.

Center of gravity location again adversely affects stability when moved aft. The static stability at 30 per cent center of gravity is less than that existing at 20 per cent, as evident from the curve slopes at trim. Instability tendencies are indicated by the figure in the low- and high-speed ranges. If the speed were increased to the unstable range, the airplane by itself would go into a dive and never recover. Likewise, if a low enough speed is approached the airplane will completely stall and could then easily go into a spin unless corrective action is taken by the pilot. Instability in the low-speed range is associated with the wing maximum lift coefficient, wake, or nonlinear elevator hinge moments (that is, high trim deflections). At high speed, it is often caused by surface deformation.

In order to avoid flutter the product of inertia about the hinge and airplane centerline axes must

be zero. However, by adding an unbalanced bob weight to the control system on the airplane centerline at or near the fuselage primary node, this criterion will not be violated. Curve (a) in Figure 17:18 shows a stable airplane, and curve

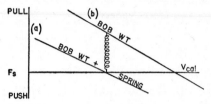

Fig. 17:18.   Effect of bob weight and springs on elevator stick force curve

(b) illustrates the new stick forces by adding this static unbalance. Note that for the same trim tab setting a new trim speed results, but the degree of stability is essentially the same. If the trim tab is reset to trim at the original speed, the stick free stability would be increased and a steeper slope would be shown on the figure. This results from effectively weighting the elevator downward and produces a greater restoring moment due to the tail and hence greater stability. The free float angle of the elevator has changed to a more nose-down tendency. During acceleration, even greater stability would result.

Suppose the stability in level flight was satisfactory originally. Then a spring could be added to neutralize the bob weight effect, and curve b would be pulled back again to curve a, leaving the level flight stick free static stability unchanged. Since accelerations will affect the bob weight but not the spring, an increase in stability under accelerated flight would be gained with no change in stability under level flight conditions. Obviously, weights or springs will not affect stick fixed stability. Inverted flight is not affected objectionably as high accelerations would be extremely abnormal.

Changing the angle of incidence of the stabilizer will change the trim speed, but in the range for trim the stick fixed static stability should remain unaltered. For various stabilizer incidences a series of parallel curves of elevator angle versus speed would be obtained in the trim speed range, but the stability toward the high- and low-speed ranges may be altered appreciably. This may be caused by the maximum lift characteristics at low speeds and surface distortion at high speeds. Similarly for the stick free stability. In this case the change in elevator free float angle may have a small influence in the trim range. Actual results depend upon the particular airplane arrangements and characteristics, and should not be taken for granted.

17.34 Trim Tab Effectiveness

In lieu of stick force instrumentation, static stick free stability may be evaluated by means of trim tab position versus airspeed as shown in Figure 17:19. The analogy is identical to that

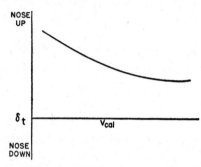

Fig. 17:19.   Elevator tab deflection versus calibration airspeed

which has been used in explaining stick force significance, except that in test, variation of tab angle rather than forces on the stick are employed. This method is inferior to that for stick force, but considerable pertinent data can be gathered.

Trim should be checked under all flight conditions to determine whether or not sufficient trim tab range is available to satisfy all conditions. In studying trim tab effectiveness a curve of stick force versus tab position may be obtained at constant flight and airspeed conditions such as

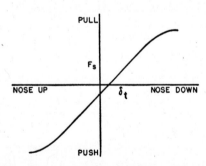

Fig. 17:20.   Elevator stick force variation with elevator tab deflection

cruising. Figure 17:20 illustrates the type of curve obtained. If the tab is ineffective at low deflections because it is in a stagnant flow region, a flat spot near the center of the curve will show up. Also the tab may be stalling at high deflections,

in which case the curve slope may flatten out at the ends as shown. Various trim tab configurations may be tested to improve such conditions.

17.4 Longitudinal Static Stability in Accelerated Flight
17.41 Stick Fixed Static Stability

Selecting the desired flight conditions, steady turns or pullups may be made at that airspeed. Stick fixed stability will be reflected in elevator position versus g as illustrated. If elevator position a in Figure 17:21 is fixed, and the normal acceleration increases to point b, then the elevator position is set for nose down tendency with respect to the new g. Thus the airplane will tend to return to point a, and positive stick fixed stability is indicated by the degree of positive slope.

For the same reasons previously given, shifting the center of gravity aft will reduce this static stability.

Yaw is important in these tests because of the effect of yaw on pitching moment. An airplane with weak directional stability may give scattered results, therefore, yaw should be measured during flight tests.

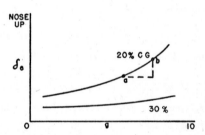

Fig. 17:21.   Elevator deflection versus normal acceleration

During windup turns at constant acceleration the airspeed should be reduced gradually to the stall. From a series of tests, cross plots at constant airspeeds should be determined.

17.42 Stick Free Static Stability

As before, stick force is used in this case, plotted against acceleration as shown in Figure 17:22. The airplane is trimmed at the desired speed in level flight, one g, and steady turns at various g's made. A pull force becoming greater as g's are applied is desired. A positive slope indicates stability because if the stick force were released the stick would immediately go forward, the nose would drop, and the acceleration would be relieved. A linear stick force gradient is desired and should be heavy enough to require considerable effort to obtain the acceleration for which the airplane was designed. Rearward center of gravity again reduces the degree of stability.

Increasing altitude is also known to decrease the stick force gradient. In some cases a negative stick force gradient has appeared at high altitudes, although this effect may not be due to altitude alone. It is also advantageous to obtain time histories of high g pullouts to study the dynamic properties of the airplane.

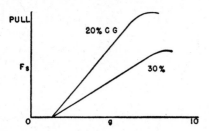

Fig. 17:22.   Elevator stick force versus normal acceleration

In case maximum lift coefficient is reached, the acceleration obtainable will be limited according to the speed at which it is obtained, in which case the force gradient will flatten out. If the tail enters the wing wake, accelerations may increase and stick forces will reduce, producing an uncontrollable condition which may be disastrous.

Stick force gradient should be essentially independent of airspeed above the stall. If an appreciable difference with variation in airspeed is discovered, it means that deflection or distortion is taking place somewhere in the airplane, control system, or control surfaces.

17.43 Mach Number Effects

Since it is extremely difficult to obtain desired data at high Mach numbers, little is known of this phenomenon. Concerning performance and stability when critical Mach numbers are reached, the changes in aerodynamic conditions and forces are severe and are always harmful. Discussion of Mach number in the foregoing paragraphs has been omitted, but the possibilities of its influence should always be kept in mind.

As an illustration of possible disastrous effects of compressibility, the case of an airplane becoming so stable in a vertical dive that recovery is impossible may be illustrated. Figure 17:23 shows a plot of the pitching moment coefficients of an airplane with stick fixed versus lift coefficient

and possible effects of Mach number determined from wind tunnel tests.

Suppose the airplane is flying level at a Mach number of .5 and a lift coefficient corresponding to point a. The airplane stalling moment must be balanced by increasing the tail moment, and the airplane may be trimmed for this condition. If the airplane then enters a vertical dive, the lift coefficient drops to zero and the conditions at point b obtain. Positive stability is indicated by the fact that the pilot must push forward on the stick to maintain this condition since the stalling moment with respect to the trim condition must be overcome by use of the elevator. As the airplane rapidly gains speed in vertical descent the Mach number increases to .75 as illustrated by point c. At this point the pilot is now pulling on the stick to counteract the diving moment with respect to the trim condition. Finally, the pilot attempts to pull out of the dive, in which case he must increase the lift coefficient at that Mach number to obtain the necessary lift for normal acceleration, and the conditions indicated by point d obtain. This point represents a very large diving moment with respect to trim, and the pilot may find that he does not have sufficient strength to pull the stick back far enough to create the required balancing tail load. Fortunately, Mach

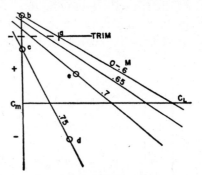

Fig. 17:23.   Effect of Mach number on pitching moment coefficient variation with lift coefficient

number at terminal velocity will reduce as altitude decreases. If the pilot is lucky enough to attain a Mach number of .7 represented by point e while sufficient altitude still remains, he may be able to recover from the dive.

It becomes apparent that the pilot may operate his trim tab during the dive to change his trim conditions to say point d. If he does so, then when he pulls out and the Mach number is further reduced, he may find himself in the reverse situation. Now a high stalling moment with respect to trim is produced, and the pilot may be physically incapable of preventing the airplane from exceeding the acceleration at which disintegration of the airplane will result.

During stability investigations previously outlined, Mach number effects or trends may be revealed by obtaining data at the same observed airspeeds, but at two widely different altitudes. Or if high lift coefficients are suspected as being a source of trouble, the gross weight may be varied over a wide range, obtaining data at constant Mach numbers by repeated observed speeds at the same altitudes. Various combinations of gross weight and altitude will provide a wide range of variation of flight conditions for purposes of analysis dictated by the particular problem at hand.

17.5 Rearward Center of Gravity for Neutral Longitudinal Stability

Having procured the above data for stick free and fixed static stability both for linear and accelerated flight at various center of gravity conditions, a plot of the slopes of these curves at trim conditions for any given condition of flight versus center of gravity position will be linear. Covering all the cases the slopes are:

(a) dF_s/dV at trim V: linear flight.
(b) $d\delta_e/dV$ at trim V: linear flight.
(c) dF_s/dg at trim V: accelerated flight.
(d) $d\delta_e/dg$ at trim V: accelerated flight.

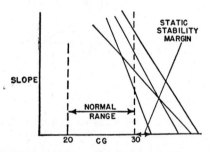

Fig. 17:24. Determination of longitudinal stability neutral points

Better points for fairing the linear flight curves are sometimes obtained after converting to coefficients. Both δ_e and F_s may be plotted against C_L in which case the slope reverses so that a positive slope implies static stability. These slopes may be plotted against center of gravity position in lieu of (a) and (b) above.

The results in Figure 17:24 show the center of gravity position at which static stability will be neutral for each condition and aft of which negative or catastrophic stability would be obtained. Static stability margin refers to the difference between the most aft center of gravity obtainable for normal operation and the most forward for neutral stability. This margin should be around 2 per cent for a fighter and more for less maneuverable aircraft.

Altitude has a detrimental effect on static stability and may cause the neutral point to move forward. Careful consideration should be given to the altitude or altitudes at which the data are desired. At the aft center of gravity critical altitude and at the forward center of gravity low altitude should be checked.

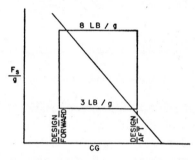

Fig. 17:25. Stick force gradient versus center of gravity location

Requirements may be illustrated in Figure 17:25 for stick force gradients. Maximum and minimum requirements of 8 and 3 lb per g are required by the Army for fighter airplanes. Since altitude will displace the curve shown parallel to itself, it is very unlikely that such limitations could be realized at all altitudes. Here a small positive slope is desired in order to stay within the " box " limits depicted.

Changing the elevator section to increase aerodynamic balance, bulged contours, or beveled trailing edges will reduce the slope of the curve of Figure 17:25, which is desirable. Adding a bob weight will shift the curve parallel either up or down depending on which way the bob weight acts.

Beveled trailing edges are apt to give trouble caused by overbalance in the small deflection range; they have not been widely used. Any changes concerning the trailing edge of a control surface will have a large affect on the results, as the aerodynamic action may be considered as analogous to trim tab effects, which are very powerful because of the large hinge moments resulting.

Again it is emphasized that as a result of the infinite range of stability modes intelligent flight testing and investigation cannot be made until the requirements are judiciously limited to the most critical specific conditions. Every desirable characteristic cannot be incorporated in one airplane.

17.6 Theoretical Considerations

Hinge moment coefficients may be studied from stick force data, since

$$C_h = \frac{M_h}{qSc} = \frac{F_s l}{qSc} = \frac{kF_s}{q} \qquad (17:1)$$

Where F_s is the stick force, l is the equivalent lever arm of the stick force acting through linkages to the elevator, c is the elevator chord, C_h is the elevator hinge moment coefficient for the moment about the hinge M_h, and q is the dynamic pressure. F_s/q, therefore, is indicative of the hinge moment coefficient and may be plotted versus lift coefficient for the range of speeds tested. Positive slopes indicate positive static stick free stability. Note that free air dynamic pressure is used, while the actual q over the tail may be appreciably less and may also vary according to the relative position of the wing wake.

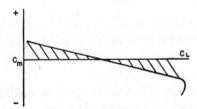

Fig. 17:26.   Airplane pitching moment coefficient versus lift coefficient

Again looking at the pitching moment curve for the complete airplane for fixed controls from wind tunnel tests, the required change in tail moments for trim at various speeds is indicated in Figure 17:26. Obtaining the curve of elevator position for trim in flight at various speeds is really determining the increments of elevator angle required to achieve these various tail moment changes. Hence the slope of the flight test curve is proportional to that shown in the figure for stick fixed stability:

$$\frac{d\delta_e}{dC_L} \propto \left(\frac{dC_m}{dC_L}\right)_{\text{stick fixed}} \qquad (17:2)$$

Similarly if a pitching moment or elevator hinge moment curve should be obtained in a wind tunnel for free control stability, the flight test curve of stick forces and speeds would be proportional to the pitching moment coefficient slope:

$$\frac{d(F_s/q)}{dC_L} \propto \frac{dC_h}{dC_L} \propto \left(\frac{Cd}{dC_L}\right)_{\text{stick free}} \qquad (17:3)$$

Stick fixed and free static longitudinal stability may be related by the expression

$$\left(\frac{dC_m}{dC_L}\right)_{\text{free}} = \left(\frac{dC_m}{dC_L}\right)_{\text{fixed}} \left(1 - \frac{\partial C_h}{\partial \alpha} \cdot \frac{\partial \delta}{\partial C_h} \cdot \frac{\partial \alpha}{\partial \delta}\right) \qquad (17:4)$$

where the static margin between fixed and free control stability is represented by the partial derivative of hinge moment coefficient variation with respect to angle of attack for elevator fixed divided by the partial derivative with respect to elevator deflection for constant angle of attack.

17.7 Forward Center of Gravity Limitations

In the foregoing analysis forward movement of center of gravity in most cases was beneficial. However, there is a definite forward limit beyond which it is undesirable to operate the airplane.

In the case of the stick force versus acceleration, the gradient may become unsatisfactorily high and a consequent practical limit may be imposed.

Another consideration is elevator stalling power, that is, the center of gravity must not be so far forward as to make it impossible to provide a tail moment with full up elevator sufficient to obtain a stalling attitude. This is the only way in which airspeed for landing can be reduced to the minimum possible value. Ground operation is also to be considered in that it should be possible to obtain a reasonably high lift coefficient, or approach a stall attitude, while on the ground at some 75 per cent of stalling airspeed. Also, accelerations resulting from high lift coefficients should not be penalized by running out of elevator control.

Approach to the stall should be gradual but unmistakable by some warning such as buffeting and airplane shaking before the actual stall develops. Stick force should gradually increase as should stick travel. Stall characteristics should not be vicious, lateral control should remain effective, and recovery should be prompt without excessive loss of altitude.

17.8 Directional Stability and Control

17.81 General

Directional stability is affected very little by center of gravity location, but may be affected by moment of inertia. In general, the gross weight and center of gravity location variables may be disregarded. In other respects, analysis may be derived from considerations similar to the treatment of longitudinal stability, but such detailed investigation is seldom required.

Short period oscillations should be checked and directional phugoids executed.

17.82 Rudder Effect and Control

Control free static directional stability may be studied by obtaining a curve of control force versus rudder deflection for various airspeed parameters.

The slope for positive stability is shown in Figure 17:27. Rudder position must be measured at the rudder itself, and excessive deflection on the control system for full rudder pedal position may be found. A practical maximum rudder pedal force is 180 lb.

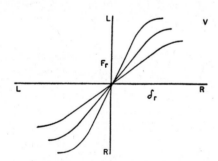

Fig. 17:27.   Rudder pedal force versus rudder deflection

Flat spots in the curves near neutral may indicate a snaking tendency, inasmuch as no centering force would be present. Flattening of the curves at either end are indicative of the approach of fin or rudder stall. Force reversals may also be revealed.

Fixed control stability is obtained in curves of yaw angle versus rudder angle at constant airspeeds. Again flat spots near neutral and hooking over of the curve extremities indicate undesirable

characteristics. As shown in Figure 17:28 positive control fixed stability is indicated. These curves should be substantially linear up to ± 15 deg. of yaw.

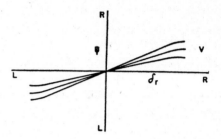

Fig. 17:28.   Yaw angle versus rudder deflection

Sufficient rudder action should be available to counteract any adverse yaw ascribable to ailerons, cross winds and slipstream rotation on the ground, and asymetrical power conditions at 10 per cent above stalling speed. Also, corrective action in spin recovery must be effected.

Flat spots or small slopes in the curves near neutral will result in snaking. This phenomenon may be investigated by initiating directional phugoids over a wide range of speeds. A bulge ahead of the rudder hinge line, large gap between fin and rudder, and wedge trailing edge rudders are some of the items which tend to aggravate snaking.

Sufficient tab should be available to trim under all flight conditions, but a large change in trim caused by power or speed is obviously objectionable especially in a fighter.

If the curve of Figure 17:28 showed increased yaw angle with small rudder deflection toward the extremities, fin stall would be indicated, while if the curves bend as shown, a rudder stall is indicated. In case the slope is too great, the vertical tail area is too small, that is, the de-stabilizing yawing moment of airplane less vertical tail because of large side areas ahead of the center of gravity is too large for the tail to counteract effectively. Dorsal fins or longitudinal fuselage spoilers would help this situation.

It may be observed here that a propeller operating in yaw produces an induced force by changing the airflow direction such as to move away from the oncoming airstream. Thus a propeller at the nose of a body produces a de-stabilizing influence, while at the rear it would tend to improve stability.

17.9 Lateral Stability and Control

Here again the general analysis may be evolved from aforementioned considerations, but the items of particular interest are control forces and rates of roll obtainable for maneuvering.

In obtaining aileron data either of two methods may be used, the results of which do not differ greatly. Rolls of 90 degrees from level flight may be executed with the rudder fixed, or the airplane may first be rolled about 60 degrees and then rolled back through level flight with co-ordinated rudder to a 60 degree opposite roll. The former is preferred. A rate of roll indicator should be used in order to obtain all data at the peak constant rate of roll obtained.

In deflecting ailerons, various amounts of chain should be fastened to the stick at the center of force application by the pilot's hand to limit the deflection to various desired constant values. The chain force will not be recorded by instrumentation measuring the bending moment of the control stick. Aileron position should be measured at each aileron.

Analysis of free stick static stability from Figure 17:29 is obvious. Forces should be light compared to other controls as 50 lb in a lateral direc-

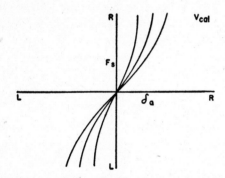

Fig. 17:29. Aileron stick force versus aileron deflection

tion represents a practical limitation of capability for a control stick. Hydraulic boost and pressure balanced ailerons are being used successfully at the present time to lighten the aileron force required. Pressure balance on ailerons is very sensitive to leaks of any sort, such as grommet drain holes, porosity of fabric, end seals, and gaps. Also, bending the wing trailing edge skin ahead of the ailerons inward or outward alters the static pressures to which the pressure balances are vented and changes the aileron hinge moments considerably. The effects of differential employed

in ailerons could bear investigation in attempting to improve their effectiveness per unit of applied force.

Response to ailerons should be immediate and forces should build up proportional to their deflection without exceeding the specified force limit at the highest speed and deflection at which operation is expected. Bulge aileron contours ahead of the hinge line will tend to lighten the forces for low deflections, while a bulge aft will lighten the whole stick force gradient. Variation in moment of inertia about the longitudinal axis for various alternate wing loads should not be overlooked.

During side slips it should be necessary to use aileron action to force the side slip by counteracting the lateral righting moment caused by the effect of dihedral in yaw. With rudder locked in neutral it is not unusual for full aileron deflection at 10 per cent above stalling speed to produce 20 degrees of yaw.

The most important aileron characteristic in a fighter is rate of roll. This should be noted independently of the wing tip helix angle, which is usually taken as a criterion:

$$\phi = \frac{Pb}{168\,V} = \text{radians} \qquad (17:5)$$

where P is rate of roll in degrees per second, b is wing span in feet, the constant is for converting mph to feet per second, the wing span to semispan, degrees into radians, and V is true airspeed in mph.

If rates of roll at constant aileron deflections are plotted against airspeed a curve similar to that illustrated in Figure 17:30 will result. The

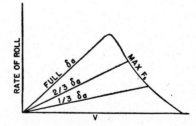

Fig. 17:30.   Rate of roll versus true airspeed for various aileron deflections

rate of roll for a constant aileron deflection varies linearly with velocity, indicating constant helix angle at the wing tip. Effectively the wing is twisted and the action is analogous to a screw entering wood where the helix angle is independent of the rate of rotation. Therefore, the slope of the curve is proportional to the helix angle, and smaller aileron deflections result in smaller helix angles.

The outer limit of the curves is imposed by the aileron stick force available such that if the force is constant the aileron deflection will decrease with increasing speed and will result in slower rates of roll.

In data analysis the calculated helix angle ϕ should be determined for each test point and plotted versus aileron position as shown in Figure 17:31. It will be found that one faired curve may

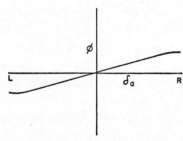

Fig. 17:31.   Wing tip helix angle versus aileron deflection

be drawn to represent all the various airspeeds.

From this curve and that for stick forces the final curves for presentation of the data may be determined. Imposing a stick force limit, points may be used from the two curves to obtain plots of aileron position, rate of roll, and helix angle all versus airspeed. The latter curve is illustrated in Figure 17:32 showing constant values of ϕ up to the speed at which allowable force will no longer give full aileron deflection.

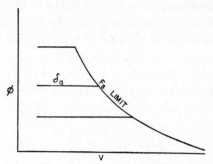

Fig. 17:32.   Wing tip helix angle versus true airspeed

For good aileron characteristics all airplanes should be able to attain a helix angle of .07 radians while for a fighter a value of .09 is desirable. This maximum rolling velocity should occur within .2 seconds after full aileron deflection is attained.

It should be emphasized that the structural design limits should be investigated before conducting aileron tests at high speeds. During tests where the aileron deflections may exceed the structural design limits, the aileron deflections should be limited by stops so that the pilot cannot impose dangerous loads on the structure.

Part Two

Jet-propelled Airplanes

THE BELL XP-83 JET-PROPELLED FIGHTER POWERED BY TWO GENERAL ELECTRIC TYPE I-40 TURBO-JET ENGINES

CHAPTER 18

TURBO-JET-PROPULSION ENGINE CHARACTERISTICS

18.1 Description of the Engine

The Whittle jet propulsion engine is named after Group Captain Frank Whittle of the Royal Air Force who produced his first successful jet propulsion engine in 1937 after more than five years of experimentation. Some four years later the first flight with this type of unit was made in England.

Figure 18:1 shows the fundamental arrangement of this turbo-jet engine. Atmospheric air enters the front of the nacelle, which is divided into two compartments, fore and aft. The forward compartment is designed to convert the velocity energy of the air into pressure energy with the minimum possible increase in temperature above that caused by adiabatic compression.

This air enters the engine compressor. A small leakage of air into the aft nacelle compartment provides for ventilation inasmuch as it contains the flame tubes and hot tailpipe.

Compression of the air is provided by a centrifugal blower operating at a compression ratio of some 4:1. This compressed air is fed into the flame tubes where combustion is consummated by the introduction of fuel, such as kerosene, as a continuous controlled flow. Addition of energy in the form of heat increases the specific volume of the combustion products which results in a high flow velocity. These gases after passing through a nozzle and vaned diaphragm drive the gas turbine wheel which, being connected to the blower by a solid shaft, in turn drives the com-

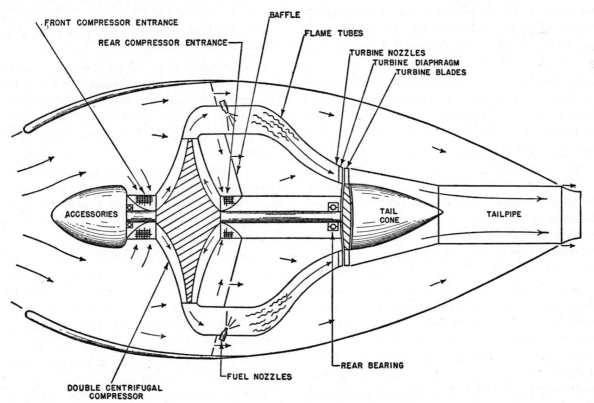

Fig. 18:1. Schematic of Whittle type turbo-jet engine

pressor. In this process primarily pressure energy is consumed, but high exhaust gas velocities still obtain. The exhaust gases are then allowed to leave the tailpipe in a rearward direction. Thrust, therefore, results from the change of momentum, the air being taken aboard at airplane velocity and expelled at a much higher velocity.

The main difference between the Whittle gas turbine engine and gas turbines used as prime movers is in the design of the turbine. In the former, the velocity energy is utilized as a thrust force, while in the latter the turbine is designed to absorb the velocity energy also in the turbine, thus converting it into shaft horsepower. This could still be done in the case of an airplane, but the shaft horsepower would then have to be converted into thrust by driving a conventional propeller. Such a gas turbine engine has a larger " exhaust pipe " because of the much lower exhaust velocities.

Combustion in the jet propulsion engine is initiated by a spark plug during the starting cycle, but during operation continuous combustion is self-supporting. This combustion is a constant pressure process, the highest in the cycle being that at the compressor discharge.

Thrust is controlled by varying the quantity of fuel burned. By varying the fuel pressure, the amount of fuel injected through the nozzles will vary to change the rpm of the unit, its mass flow, and therefore the jet thrust.

This engine like all other engines uses the oxygen of the atmosphere to support combustion. Consequently, the altitude at which thrust may be obtained is limited by the atmospheric density. Since this unit is essentially a turbine, it will cease to deliver thrust in the vicinity of 67,000 ft, approximately the limitation of a conventional engine with turbo-driven supercharging.

Although specific reference is made here to the centrifugal blower type of turbo-jet engine, it is also pointed out that the axial flow supercharger is essentially the same, differing only in details. Dimensional analysis and general engine characteristics apply to both types. The only significant differences are to be found in the lower frontal area and higher inlet velocities of the axial flow type and in some difference in engine weight per pound of thrust. Installation details differ, but performances are comparable.

Rocket propulsion is distinctly different from jet propulsion as described, in that the oxygen for the cycle is carried as well as the fuel. Thrust is delivered by the same momentum reaction of the issuing gases, but the rocket will operate independently of the atmosphere.

18.2 Advantages of Jet Propulsion

The Whittle jet propulsion engine is very simple compared to the conventional engine and its potentialities in respect to performance are promising. These advantages and desirable characteristics can be summarized as follows:

(a) *High speed and altitude performance.* The higher the speed the greater the efficiency of jet propulsion, and speeds at least 100 mph greater than presently obtained with the conventional airplane are possible. Also as a result of the high altitude characteristics, very high speeds are possible at higher altitudes.

Propulsive efficiency may be taken as the ratio of the power output, $M(V_j - V)V$, to the power input, $M(V_j - V)V + M(V_j - V)^2/2$, since the kinetic energy of the exhaust gases is lost energy.

$$\eta = \frac{\text{output}}{\text{input}} = \frac{2 V}{V + V_j} \qquad (18:1)$$

For airplane velocity, V, equal to 0, the efficiency is zero. When $V = V_j/4$, $\eta = .40$; $V = V_j/2$, $\eta = .67$; $V = 3 V_j/4$, $\eta = .86$; and when $V = V_j$, $\eta = 1.00$. For propeller driven airplanes, the practical maximum speed is around 500 mph, as at higher speeds propulsive efficiency falls off to a prohibitive degree because of compressibility effects.

(b) *Simplicity.* One rotating part replaces the hundreds of moving parts required by other engines. In flight the throttle represents the only engine control. There is no ignition system, propeller, carburetor, oil cooling system, or engine cooling system. All the attendant complications are absent. Installation becomes extremely simple.

(c) *Long life.* Since there is no reciprocating action or sliding motion, there is no wear. Maintenance is a minimum and life a maximum. Lubrication for the two ball or roller bearings plus the accessory gears is simple to provide, no oil cooling problems being present.

(d) *No fire hazard.* Use of nonvolatile, noninflammable fuels preclude the possibility of fire.

Fuels are cheap, and apparently no icing difficulties are encountered.

(e) *Design adaptation.* Eliminating the propeller opens up new fields to the design engineer since engine or propeller clearance problems dictate no special arrangement. Location of the power plant is practically independent of its requirements.

(f) *Simple operation.* Since only one engine control, the throttle, is necessary, the simplest possible operation ensues. No warm up period nor operational limitations other than rpm and tailpipe temperature are imposed, thereby practically eliminating attention on the part of the pilot.

(g) *No vibration.* The absence of reciprocation or power impulses eliminates vibration.

(h) *Light weight.* Simplicity of the unit results in a very light weight power plant such that a much larger ratio of static thrust to engine weight is possible.

The only serious disadvantage is the high rate of fuel consumption especially at low altitude. However, at high altitudes where the thrust per unit of true speed decreases, fuel consumption is comparable to conventional airplanes. Further improvements in blower and turbine efficiencies and especially in metallurgy will greatly improve engine performance and to an appreciable extent fuel consumption.

18.3 The Nernst Cycle

The Nernst cycle, which may be used to represent the cycle of a Whittle jet propulsion engine, is shown in the $P - v$ diagram of Figure 18:2.

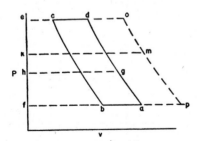

Fig. 18:2.   The Nernst cycle

Point *b* represents atmospheric air which is adiabatically compressed to about four atmospheres along curve $b - c$. From *c* to *d* fuel is introduced and burned at constant pressure, thereby increasing considerably its specific vol-

ume. These gases are then expanded back to atmospheric pressure where the specific volume is considerably larger than that of the initial air.

The area *b-f-e-c* enclosed in the figure represents the work, including flow energy, required in compressing the air. Since this energy to drive the compressor must be delivered by the turbine, an area *h-e-d-g* represents the same amount of energy put into the turbine. Area *a-f-h-g* represents the energy available for output. In the jet engine this energy exists as heat energy and kinetic energy of the gases issuing from the tailpipe.

Limitations of the engine are twofold. First, the rpm attainable is limited by compressibility effects of the blower, which obtain before structural limitations prevail. Second, a metallurgical limitation is encountered in that a relatively low temperature must not be exceeded in order that the structural properties of the turbine blade material will not be impaired. As metallurgical research provides higher temperature materials, more and more thrust will be available from the same engine design by introducing more fuel. This may be represented in the diagram by extending the expansion process out to curve *o-p*, no further work being required by the compressor. The net result is to make tremendously greater output possible as represented by the area *p-f-k-m*. At present the fuel-air ratio is approximately 1:60, while optimum combustion would still be obtained at a ratio of 1:15, or four times as much fuel.

Increased output may also be obtained by increasing the compression ratio, but this method would entail additional mechanical complications, and in the final analysis the same temperature limitation will be encountered.

18.4 Dimensional Analysis of Engine Characteristics
18.41 *Definition of Variables Involved*

In general, the material upon which this section is based may be found in references 26 and 30. The purpose here is to show how dimensional analysis provides a basis for determining the relationships between all the variables involved so that intelligent analysis of experimental data may be performed. An understanding of the assumptions and limitations of the various parameters used in data analysis is thus provided.

The variables involved in a discussion of turbo-jet engines may be represented in terms of the dimensions of mass, length, and time as given in Table 15.

TABLE 15.   VARIABLES AFFECTING ENGINE PERFORMANCE

Variable	Symbol	Dimensional units
RPM	N	t^{-1}
Airplane airspeed	V	Lt^{-1}
Linear dimension	D	L
Compressor entrance total pressure	P_e	$ML^{-1}t^{-2}$
Compressor entrance total temperature	T_e	L^2t^{-2}
Net thrust (or gross jet thrust)	F (or F_j)	MLt^{-2}
Rate of fuel consumption	W_f	MLt^{-3}
Rate of mass airflow	M_a	Mt^{-1}
Free air temperature	T	Lt^{-2}
Free air pressure	P	$ML^{-1}t^{-2}$
Nacelle entrance velocity	V_e	Lt^{-1}

When dealing with units of the same type, D is constant and will be considered only for its dimensional characteristics. This linear dimension may be considered as describing the size of the engine, for example, by the diameter of the turbine wheel.

Note that temperature has been assigned the units of velocity squared, which is consistent with energy relationships and results in a dimensionless gas constant per unit of mass.

All of the variables involved in determining the jet thrust, weight of fuel flow, and mass airflow characteristics for a turbo-jet engine may be completely expressed as some functions of the form:

$$f_1(F_j, N, P, P_e, T_e, D) = 0 \qquad (18:2)$$

$$f_2(W_f, N, P, P_e, T_e, D) = 0 \qquad (18:3)$$

$$f_3(M_a, N, P, P_e, T_e, D) = 0 \qquad (18:4)$$

Thus the jet thrust, fuel consumption, and mass airflow are completely determined by the size of the engine, the rpm at which it is operating, the compressor entrance pressure and temperature conditions, and the pressure to which it is exhausting.

18.42 Example of Dimensional Analysis Solution

From reference 27 the Buckingham π theorem may be stated thus: Given n variables in m fundamental units; if the equation $f(x_1, \cdots x_n) = 0$ is a complete equation, the solution has the form $G\ (\pi_1, \pi_2, \cdots \pi_{n-m}) = 0$, where the π's are dimensionless products of the variables. In general, $n - m$ of the exponents in each product are arbitrary.

For example, in equation 18:2 there are six variables and three fundamental units (M, L, and t), so there are three dimensionless products:

$$\pi_1 = F_j{}^{a1} \cdot N^{b1} \cdot P^{c1} \cdot P_e{}^{d1} \cdot T_e{}^{e1} \cdot D^{f1}$$

$$\pi_2 = F_j{}^{a2} \cdot N^{b2} \cdot P^{c2} \cdot P_e{}^{d2} \cdot T_e{}^{e2} \cdot D^{f2}$$

$$\pi_3 = F_j{}^{a3} \cdot N^{b3} \cdot P^{c3} \cdot P_e{}^{d3} \cdot T_e{}^{e3} \cdot D^{f3}$$

We may assign the following exponents to three of the variables in each product:

$$a1 = 1 \qquad b1 = 0 \qquad c1 = 0$$
$$a2 = 0 \qquad b2 = 1 \qquad c2 = 0$$
$$a3 = 0 \qquad b3 = 0 \qquad c3 = 1$$

Consequently, the three products become:

$$\pi_1 = F_j \cdot P_e{}^{d1} \quad T_e{}^{e1} \cdot D^{f1}$$

$$\pi_2 = N \cdot P_e{}^{d2} \quad T_e{}^{e2} \cdot D^{f2}$$

$$\pi_3 = P \cdot P_e{}^{d3} \quad T_e{}^{e3} \cdot D^{f3}$$

and the remaining exponents are to be determined so that the products are dimensionless, for example, for π_1:

$$\text{Dimension } \pi_1 = M^0 L^0 T^0$$
$$= (MLt^{-2})(M^{d1}L^{-d1}t^{-2d1})(L^{2e1}t^{-2e1})(L^{f1})$$

Exponent of $M = 1 + d1 = 0$

Exponent of $L\ = 1 - d1 + 2e1 + f1 = 0$

Exponent of $t\ \ = -2 - 2d1 - 2e1 = 0$

Solving these three equations for the three unknowns

$$d1 = -1 \qquad e1 = 0 \qquad f1 = -2$$

and therefore

$$\pi_1 = \frac{F_j}{P_e D^2}$$

In a similar manner the value of the products π_2 and π_3 will be found to be

$$\pi_2 = \frac{ND}{\sqrt{T_e}}$$

$$\pi_3 = \frac{P_e}{P}$$

It has now been established that equation 18:2 has the form

$$G_1\left[\frac{F_j}{P_e D^2}, \frac{ND}{\sqrt{T_e}}, \frac{P_e}{P}\right] = 0$$

Assuming D to be constant and solving for the jet thrust term:

$$\frac{F_j}{P_e} = f_1\left(\frac{N}{\sqrt{T_e}}, \frac{P_e}{P}\right)$$

18.43 Characteristics Independent of Airspeed

By the simple process of dimensional analysis described in the preceding section, the forms of equations 18:2, 18:3, and 18:4 will be found to be

$$\frac{F_j}{P_e} = f_1\left(\frac{N}{\sqrt{T_e}}, \frac{P_e}{P}\right) \tag{18:5}$$

$$\frac{M_a\sqrt{T_e}}{P_e} = f_2\left(\frac{N}{\sqrt{T_e}}, \frac{P_e}{P}\right) \tag{18:6}$$

$$\frac{W_f}{P_e\sqrt{T_e}} = f_3\left(\frac{N}{\sqrt{T_e}}, \frac{P_e}{P}\right) \tag{18:7}$$

The exact functions or equations for determining jet thrust, fuel consumption, and mass airflow are stil obscure. In lieu of an analytical solution we may resort to an empirical determination of these functions, since the engine may be operated on a thrust stand, and all of the variables may be measured. Difficulty would be encountered only in attempting to vary compressor entrance pressures appreciably from atmospheric. Once these functions are determined and plotted in curve form it is a simple matter to determine these engine characteristics under widely varying conditions, such as at altitude, for instance.

18.44 Characteristics Involving Airspeed

In an actual installation in flight the compressor entrance conditions will depend upon the velocity of the free air, the free air conditions, and the design of the air intake system. For a perfect installation the impact pressure and temperature at the compressor entrance would be determined by the adiabatic compression values according to Bernoulli's equation.

$$P_e = P + q_c = f(P,T,V) \text{ — see eq. 4:2.}$$

$$T_e = T + CV^2 = f(T,V) \text{ — see eq. 7:2.}$$

It is a well-established fact that friction losses and heat conduction and radiation make the flow changes nonadiabatic. The pressure will be lower and the temperature usually higher than the theoretical values, both effects tending to reduce the thrust output of the engine. Recovery factors for a given installation would simply alter the ideal conditions as follows:

$$P_e = P + K_1 q_c \qquad (K_1 < 1.0)$$

$$T_e = T + K_2 CV^2 \qquad (K_2 > 1.0)$$

Although the recovery factors, K_1 and K_2, will be found to vary only slightly in flight, it is sufficient for our purpose to use the more general relations

$$P_e = f(F_j, N, P, T, V)$$

$$T_e = f(F_j, N, P, T, V)$$

Substituting these compressor entrance functions in equations 18:2, 18:3, and 18:4 results in functions dependent upon free air conditions:

$$f_1(F_j, N, P, T, V, D) = 0 \tag{18:8}$$

$$f_2(W_f, N, P, T, V, D) = 0 \tag{18:9}$$

$$f_3(M_a, N, P, T, V, D) = 0 \tag{18:10}$$

from which dimensional analysis will show:

$$\frac{F_j}{P} = f_1\left(\frac{N}{\sqrt{T}}, \frac{V}{\sqrt{T}}\right) \tag{18:11}$$

$$\frac{W_f}{P\sqrt{T}} = f_2\left(\frac{N}{\sqrt{T}}, \frac{V}{\sqrt{T}}\right) \tag{18:12}$$

$$\frac{M_a\sqrt{T}}{P} = f_3\left(\frac{N}{\sqrt{T}}, \frac{V}{\sqrt{T}}\right) \tag{18:13}$$

Knowing that the ram drag, or initial momentum of the air, must be subtracted from the jet thrust to obtain net thrust:

$$F = F_j - M_a V \tag{18:14}$$

or

$$\frac{F}{P} = \frac{F_j}{P} - \frac{M_a\sqrt{T}}{P} \times \frac{V}{\sqrt{T}} = f_4\left(\frac{N}{\sqrt{T}}, \frac{V}{\sqrt{T}}\right) \tag{18:15}$$

From this expression a graphical plot of these parameters as shown in Figure 18:3 will result.

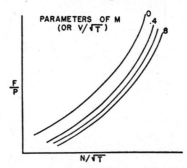

Fig. 18:3. Universal thrust-rpm polars

Such a graph illustrates the universal solution for net thrust available in terms of the atmospheric conditions, airspeed, and rpm. Note that $V/\sqrt{T} = 44.85 M$, from equation 7:5. Such a set of data would be very difficult to obtain in flight as none of the parameters can be held constant during a series of runs. The significance of these parameters, however, is of the utmost importance as they form the basis for data analysis. Similarly the fuel and airflow parameters are to be kept in mind.

From the standpoint of flight testing and performance analysis it is very simple and convenient to work with free atmospheric values. However, the engine manufacturer, in order to present engine data in a form independent of any installation, will still use compressor entrance values, which are independent of airspeed.

Since mass airflow may be written in terms of nacelle entrance conditions as $\rho A V_e^2$, equation 18:13 may be revised and the nacelle entrance velocity ratio function determined:

$$\frac{V_e}{V} = f_5 \left(\frac{N}{\sqrt{T}}, \frac{V}{\sqrt{T}} \right) \qquad (18:16)$$

18.5 Engine Characteristics

By dimensional analysis it has been shown that thrust divided by entrance pressure is a function of rpm divided by the square root of the absolute entrance temperature for static conditions. Also, the other relations involving airflow and fuel flow have been derived.

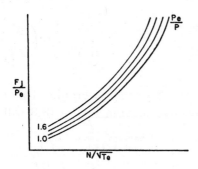

Fig. 18:4.   Jet thrust parameter characteristics

If an engine is operated on a thrust stand, the basic thrust curve shown in Figure 18:4 may be obtained. Subscript e represents compressor entrance conditions and P represents atmospheric pressure. For static conditions, when entrance conditions are atmospheric, the curve for $P_e/P = 1.0$ results, and the jet thrust, F_j, is the static thrust obtained.

However, in flight both the entrance pressure and temperature conditions will be higher than atmospheric because of adiabatic compression. Entrance velocity for a centrifugal compressor is

of small magnitude compared to the airplane velocity. Curves for various parameters of P_e/P are supplied by the engine manufacturer from thermodynamic analysis for the particular engine. In flight the entrance conditions must be measured to evaluate the installation, obtaining curves of ΔP versus V_{cal}, and Δt versus V as illustrated in Figure 18:5. Here ΔP is the average total head at

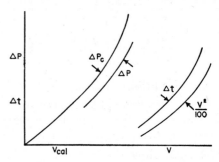

Fig. 18:5.   Compressor entrance pressure and temperature rise characteristics

the compressor entrance above the free atmospheric pressure. Many points at the inlets must be taken to obtain the complete distribution. Recovery pressures of 90 per cent of the dynamic pressure are possible, and the temperature rise should be very little above that due to adiabatic compression (equation 7:3). If conditions are poor, the cause should be investigated and corrected. A glance at Figure 18:4 reveals the detrimental effect of low entrance pressures and high temperatures on jet thrust.

Since tailpipe, or gross jet, thrust is the momentum reaction of the gases leaving the tailpipe, the momentum change required to take the air on board must be subtracted in order to obtain the propulsive thrust

$$F = M_g V_j - M_a V = F_j - M_a V, \; (V = \text{ft/sec}) \qquad (18:17)$$

Figure 18:6 represents the curve expressing mass airflow or air consumption on the thrust stand for $P_e/P = 1.0$. Parameters of P_e/P may be obtained from thermodynamic studies and empirical data, supplied by the engine manufacturer. The complete expression for propulsive thrust in terms of the values from Figures 18:4 and 18:6 for the flight conditions then depends upon the speed parameter:

$$F = P_e \left[\frac{F_j}{P_e} - \frac{M_a \sqrt{T_e}}{P_e} \left(\frac{V}{\sqrt{T_e}} \right) \right] = F_j - M_a V \qquad (18:18)$$

Thus with the aid of the engine manufacturer's curves in the form of Figures 18:4 and 18:6 and the characteristic curves for the particular installation, Figure 18:5, the propulsive thrust for any pressure, temperature, rpm, and true airspeed conditions may be calculated. Actually the

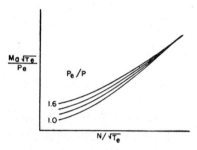

Fig. 18:6.   Mass airflow parameter characteristics

jet or gross thrust is the rate of change of momentum of the exhaust gases $= (M_a + M_f)V_j$. Since the fuel is already on board only the momentum change required to take the air aboard, $M_a V$, must be subtracted to obtain propulsive thrust. According to the calculation methods just

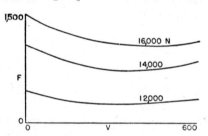

Fig. 18:7.   Variation of thrust with airspeed

given, propulsive thrust decreases with increase in velocity until some value is reached when the increase in gross thrust caused by higher air mass flow and jet velocities balances the ram drag effect. Thereafter a slight gain in thrust obtains. Figure 18:7 shows a typical plot of thrust characteristics at a given altitude.

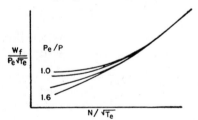

Fig. 18:8.   Fuel flow parameter characteristics

Fuel flow may be presented in terms of the parameters as illustrated in Figure 18:8. Likewise, the tailpipe temperature as measured, which includes the adiabatic rise caused by velocity at

the particular pickup in the tailpipe, may be presented as in Figure 18:9. The manufacturer specifies a maximum tailpipe temperature allowable for operation.

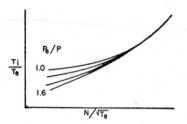

Fig. 18:9.   Tailpipe temperature parameter characteristics

Finally, the complete engine characteristics at a given altitude may be presented on one plot for convenience. Basically, lines of constant airflow and fuel flow are plotted on the propulsive thrust curve of Figure 18:7. These curves are calculated for a given ram recovery factor and adiabatic temperature rise from standard atmospheric conditions and are shown in Figure 18:10. Knowing the airplane characteristics the thrust required polar may be superimposed thereon. This is a

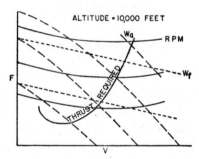

Fig. 18:10.   Turbo-jet engine performance characteristics

convenient method for performance determination. Level flight performance in relation to speed, range, endurance, and minimum rpm is easily determined. Also, climb performance may be obtained by calculations based on the excess thrust available. Polars at various gross weights may be included to find its effects. Such an analysis is valuable in numerous respects, especially in the design stages.

Glancing back at the previous figures, it is apparent that the values and units of the parameters are obscure in meaning. Therefore, a much more intelligible presentation will result if the pressure and temperature units in the parameters are made nondimensional by dividing them by their sea level values. In this way all thrust, rpm, fuel flow, and other basic quantities will be represented as the actual sea level values, and they may be converted to any desired altitude values knowing the altitude pressure and temperature ratios.

For example, if $F = 1,000$ lb at sea level ($P = 29.92$ in. Hg), then $F/P = 33.4$ lb/in. Hg. However, $F/(P/P_0) = 1,000$ lb and at 30,000 ft, $P/P_0 = .296$, so for the same parameter value F will be 296 lb.

18.6 Tailpipe Thrust Determination

18.61 Instrumentation

Tailpipe measurements required for calculation of propulsive thrust in flight are very simple. Readings of impact pressure and temperature in the tailpipe plus atmospheric pressure and airspeed are the minimum required. (See Figure 18:11.)

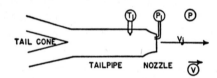

Fig. 18:11. Tailpipe impact pressure and temperature measurement

Impact pressure at one point does not represent the mean average, so the subscript i for the indicated value is used. Similarly, the temperature pickup gives an indicated temperature lower than the impact temperature depending upon its recovery factor, K. (See section 7.2.) Atmospheric pressure is obtained from the pressure altitude of test, and airplane airspeed is also obtained in the normal manner.

Propulsive thrust consists of the jet thrust minus the ram drag. The former value is obtained from the average impact and atmospheric pressures only, while temperature and fuel consumption are required to evaluate the air consumption appearing in the latter value. Tailpipe static pressure may be used for the latter calculation, but the method given here does not require this measurement, thus eliminating the necessity for this additional datum.

The derivation of the following is essentially in accord with one of the methods developed by the General Electric Company.

18.62 Critical Pressure Ratio

Critical pressure ratio for sonic velocity in a nozzle throat has already been derived in section 3.3. Equation 3:15 may be rewritten here in terms of the ratio of chamber pressure, which in this case is the *mean* tailpipe impact or total pressure, to atmospheric pressure:

$$\frac{P_{im}}{P} = \left(\frac{\gamma + 1}{2}\right)^{\gamma/(\gamma-1)} = 1.852 \quad (18:19)$$

where $\gamma = 1.33$ for gases in the high temperature range under consideration.

Thus, if the mean tailpipe impact pressure is less than 1.852 times the atmospheric pressure of exhaust, subsonic nozzle throat, or jet, velocities obtain. At or above a ratio of 1.852 the jet velocity will be equal to sonic velocity corresponding to the static temperature in the nozzle throat, and in a convergent nozzle such as this, sonic velocity cannot be exceeded. Therefore, the nozzle throat pressure will rise above atmospheric, and this pressure difference at the nozzle exit will result in a thrust force

$$F_j = \frac{W_g V_c}{g} + \Delta P A_t \quad (18:20)$$

where $V_c = V_j$ for critical pressure ratio
       $= $ ft/sec
       $\Delta P = P_{im}/1.852 - P = $ lb/in.^{2}
       $A_t = $ nozzle throat area $= $ in.^{2}

18.63 Determination of Jet Thrust

(a) *Subsonic flow*

Jet thrust is calculated from the weight flow of the gases and the jet velocity by the equation

$$F_j = \frac{W_g V_j}{g} = \text{lb} \quad (18:21)$$

Thermodynamic expressions for gas flow, velocity, and specific volume may be written

$$W_g = \frac{A_t V_j}{144 v_t} = \text{lb/sec} \quad (18:22)$$

$$V_j = \sqrt{2 gR \left(\frac{\gamma}{\gamma - 1}\right) Y_a (T_s)_t} = \text{ft/sec} \quad (18:23)$$

$$v_t = \frac{R(T_s)_t}{144(P_s)_t} = \frac{R(T_s)_t}{144 P} = \text{ft}^3/\text{lb} \quad (18:24)$$

where

v_t = specific volume at nozzle throat = ft³/lb

$R = 53.6$

$$Y_a = \left(\frac{P_{im}}{P}\right)^{(\gamma-1)/\gamma} - 1$$

$(T_s)_t$ = static temperature at nozzle throat
= ° R

$(P_s)_t$ = static pressure at nozzle throat = lb/in.²

All velocities are in ft/sec and temperatures in degrees Rankine throughout this chapter. For subsonic flow considered here the nozzle throat pressure is equal to atmospheric. Also

$$P = \frac{P_{im}}{(Y_a + 1)^{\gamma/(\gamma-1)}} \qquad (18{:}25)$$

Equations 18:21 through 18:25 may be combined in the final form for subsonic jet velocities:

$$\frac{F_j}{A_t P_{im}} = \frac{8.06\, Y_a}{(Y_a + 1)^{4.03}} \quad \text{for} \quad \frac{P_{im}}{P} < 1.852 \qquad (18{:}26)$$

This expression may be plotted as $F_j/A_t P_{im}$ versus P_{im}/P up to a value of 1.852 of the latter. Such a curve would then be used for calculating jet thrust very simply from known values of nozzle area, mean tailpipe impact pressure, and atmospheric pressure. However, the fact that the indicated impact pressure does not represent the mean value remains to be considered and is developed in section 18.65.

(b) *Sonic flow*

For the case of sonic velocity as given in equation 18:19, the value of Y_a reduces to:

$$Y_a = \frac{\gamma - 1}{2} = .165 \qquad (18{:}27)$$

Substituting this value in equation 18:26 gives

$$\frac{F_j}{A_t P_{im}} = .718 \quad \text{for} \quad \frac{P_{im}}{P} = 1.852 \qquad (18{:}28)$$

(c) " *Supersonic* " *flow conditions*

For greater pressure ratios the exhaust velocity in a convergent nozzle will remain constant, so the velocity thrust component is determined directly from this equation. Then the remaining pressure thrust will be

Pressure thrust $= A_t[(P_s)_t - P] \qquad (18{:}29)$

The expression for the atmospheric pressure is

given by equation 18:25, and the static pressure at the nozzle throat by

$$(P_s)_t = \frac{P_{im}}{1.852} \qquad (18{:}30)$$

Adding the velocity and pressure thrusts, using equations 28, 29, 25 and 30, the final expression for the sonic flow regime is:

$$\frac{F_j}{A_t P_{im}} = 1.26 - \frac{1}{(Y_a + 1)^{4.03}} \quad \text{for}$$

$$\frac{P_{im}}{P} > 1.852 \qquad (18{:}31)$$

An expression for determination of jet thrust for any given condition of operation is now available, and the jet thrust parameter from equations 18:26, 18:28, and 18:31 may be plotted against P_{im}/P. A correction factor then remains to be applied to correct for the difference between the average impact pressure and that measured at one point by a total head tube. Test stand results will furnish this empirical factor.

Note: To convert these three equations from pressure units in pounds per square inch to units in inches of mercury, multiply the right-hand sides by .4912.

18.64 Determination of Weight Flow of Air

From average tailpipe impact pressure, atmospheric pressure, and indicated tailpipe temperature, the weight flow of the exhaust gases may be determined. It is merely necessary then to subtract the fuel consumption to obtain the airflow. Fuel consumption may be measured or estimated, since it is less than 2 per cent of the weight flow of the exhaust gases.

(a) *Subsonic flow*

Gas weight flow for subsonic conditions is derived from the general thrust equation, having already determined the jet thrust:

$$W_g = \frac{gF_j}{V_j} \quad \text{for} \quad \frac{P_{im}}{P} < 1.852 \qquad (18{:}32)$$

From thermodynamics the velocity of a gas issuing from a converging nozzle in the subsonic range is expressed.

$$V_j = \sqrt{2\, gR\left(\frac{\gamma}{\gamma - 1}\right)(T_T)_P\left(\frac{Y_a}{Y_a + 1}\right)} \qquad (18{:}33)$$

where $(T_T)_P$ = true total tailpipe absolute temperature

It is necessary to express the true total tail-pipe temperature in terms of the indicated temperature:

$$(T_T)_P = (T_s)_P + (\Delta T_V)_P \qquad (18{:}34)$$

Where $(\Delta T_V)_P$ is the temperature equivalent of the velocity in the tailpipe, being the total temperature for stopped flow minus the static temperature in the tailpipe. (See section 7.2.)

$$(\Delta T_V)_P = Y_b(T_s)_P \qquad (18{:}35)$$

where

$$Y_b = \frac{(T_T)_P}{(T_s)_P} - 1 = \left(\frac{P_{im}}{P_s}\right)^{(\gamma-1)/\gamma} - 1 \qquad (18{:}36)$$

so

$$(T_T)_P = (T_s)_P(1 + Y_b) \qquad (18{:}37)$$

Empirically it has been determined that a bare thermocouple in the tailpipe gases has a recovery factor, K, of approximately .6, so the indicated temperature for this particular installation is

$$T_i = (T_s)_P + .6(\Delta T_V)_P$$
$$= (T_s)_P(1 + .6\,Y_b) \qquad (18{:}38)$$

Therefore:

$$(T_T)_P = T_i\left(\frac{1 + Y_b}{1 + .6\,Y_b}\right) \qquad (18{:}39)$$

Substituting this value in equation 18:33:

$$V_j = \sqrt{2\,gR\left(\frac{\gamma}{\gamma-1}\right)T_i\left(\frac{1+Y_b}{1+.6\,Y_b}\right)\left(\frac{Y_a}{Y_a+1}\right)}$$
$$(18{:}40)$$

For the range of present tailpipe velocities, the complete Y_b term will not vary more than one per cent, and it may be assumed constant. In this case a value equalling 1.011 is assumed, but a representative value for any particular type of engine should be ascertained.

$$V_j = \sqrt{2.022\,gR\left(\frac{\gamma}{\gamma-1}\right)T_i\left(\frac{Y_a}{Y_a+1}\right)}$$
$$= 119\sqrt{T_i}\,\sqrt{\frac{Y_a}{Y_a+1}} \qquad (18{:}41)$$

Equation 18:26 expressed the jet thrust for the subsonic range and 18:41 the corresponding jet velocity. Now equation 18:32 may be solved for the gas weight flow and these jet thrust and velocity values substituted into it. This result

may be rearranged in a form more suitable for plotting:

$$\frac{W_g\sqrt{T_i}}{A_t P_{im}} = 2.181\sqrt{\frac{Y_a}{(Y_a+1)^{7.06}}} \quad \text{for}$$
$$\frac{P_{im}}{P} < .1852 \qquad (18{:}42)$$

(b) *Sonic and supersonic flow conditions*

Since the critical pressure ratio for sonic velocity cannot be exceeded, the value of Y_a becomes constant accordingly. Evaluating Y_a for this condition, the above equation reduces to:

$$\frac{W_g\sqrt{T_i}}{A_t P_{im}} = .518 \quad \text{for} \quad \frac{P_{im}}{P}$$
$$= 1.582 \text{ or greater} \qquad (18{:}43)$$

Thus this parameter of gas weight flow reaches a constant value. Similar to the jet thrust parameter, this parameter may be plotted throughout the pressure ratio range. The empirical correction factor for total pressure measurement remains to be derived.

Subtraction of the fuel flow from the gas flow will determine the air consumption of the engine.

Note: To convert equations 18:42 and 18:43 from units of pounds per square inch and degrees Rankine to inches of mercury and degrees Kelvin, multiply the right-hand sides by .366.

18.65 Empirical Correction Factor

The preceding equations for jet thrust and gas weight flow have been based on a mean effective impact pressure in the tailpipe, which is a quantity not directly measurable. Rather than make a pressure distribution survey it is much easier to measure the static thrust of the unit in a test stand and determine a correction factor to be applied to the calculated thrust based on a single impact measurement. Once calibrated in this manner the impact pressure pickup should not be disturbed in order to avoid a possible change in the calibration factor. This factor will depend primarily on the immersion of the pickup from the tailpipe sidewall.

Let the pressure parameter Y calculated from the measured pressure values be denoted by the subscript A.

$$Y_A = \left(\frac{P_i}{P}\right)^{(\gamma-1)/\gamma} - 1 \qquad (18{:}44)$$

Then the calculated jet velocity based on this single indicated impact pressure would be

$$(V_j)_A = \sqrt{2\,gR\left(\frac{\gamma - 1}{\gamma}\right)Y_A(T_s)_t} \quad (18{:}45)$$

The true jet velocity has been defined in equation 18:23. By definition, the tailpipe calibration factor, k, is the ratio of these two velocities:

$$k = \frac{V_j}{(V_j)_A} \quad (18{:}46)$$

From equation 18:46 the relation between the true and calculated pressure parameters may be found:

$$Y_a = k^2 Y_A \quad (18{:}47)$$

from which

$$P_{im} = P(Y_a + 1)^{\gamma/(\gamma - 1)}$$
$$= P(k^2 Y_A + 1)^{\gamma/(\gamma - 1)} \quad (18{:}48)$$

From equation 18:44:

$$P = \frac{P_i}{(Y_A + 1)^{\gamma/(\gamma - 1)}} \quad (18{:}49)$$

And finally the relation between the mean effective and the indicated impact pressures is

$$P_{im} = P_i\left(\frac{k^2 Y_A + 1}{Y_A + 1}\right)^{4.03} \quad (18{:}50)$$

This equation provides a means of determining the relation which exists between the true and indicated impact pressure values once k has been evaluated. P_i is measured directly, and with the value of atmospheric pressure Y_A can be calculated.

The jet thrust may be measured on a thrust stand for subsonic velocities and represented by equation 18:26:

$$F_j = 8.06\,\frac{A_t P_{im} Y_a}{(Y_a + 1)^{4.03}} \quad (18{:}51)$$

Substituting equations 18:50 and 18:47 into this and solving the result for the correction factor gives

$$k = \sqrt{\frac{F_j(Y_A + 1)^{4.03}}{8.06\,A_t P_i Y_A}} \quad (18{:}52)$$

All of the values in this expression are obtained from measurement. This k factor when applied to jet thrust remains constant within 1.0 to 2 per cent for a given impact pressure tap configuration.

When it is applied to the weight flow of gas, it is accurate to within 3 per cent. Since the weight flow term is used only in calculating ram drag, which is roughly only one quarter of the net thrust, its effect on net thrust will be of the order of .75 per cent. Consequently, the maximum error in the complete method of propulsive thrust determination should not exceed 3 per cent for accurate data.

As yet there is no method of checking the accuracy of these equations for supersonic flow nor actual flight conditions.

The small amount of cooling air required by the engine represents a drag or power loss chargeable to the engine. However, because of the small magnitude of this loss, it has been thus far neglected.

Although the accuracy of this method of thrust determination is generally satisfactory, further refinements are being made. In an experimental or unusual installation it is advisable to install a rake of total head tubes at the nozzle to determine the total head distribution, and, at the same time, static pressure measurements should be made. If the static pressure is not equal to atmospheric pressure, then an error in mass flow will result which in turn will affect the ram drag. Nozzle shape, such as conical or venturi types, will appreciably affect the static pressure. Having once investigated a new installation in detail, the relatively small inaccuracies of the simple method may be accounted for.

The final jet thrust and gas flow parameters have been plotted in Figures 18:12 and 18:13 for various correction factors in terms of the ratio of the indicated impact pressure divided by the atmospheric pressure.

18.66 Sample Calculations

Given the following flight test data:
$H_p = 20{,}000$ ft.   ($P = 13.75$ in. Hg).
$V = 400$ mph.
$P_i = 24.8$ in. Hg absolute.
$W_f = 800$ lb/hr.
$k = .94$.
$A_t = 114$ in.^{2}.
$t_i = 660°C$. $T_i = 933°K$.
Calculations:
(a) $P_i/P = 24.8/13.75 = 1.803$.
(b) $F_j/.4912\,A_t P_i = .619$ from Figure 18:12a.

(c) $F_j = (.619)(.4912)(114)(24.8) = 860$ lb *gross thrust*.

(d) $W_g\sqrt{T_i}/.366\,A_t P_i = .483$ from Figure 18:13a.

(e) $W_g = (.483)(.366)(114)(24.8)/\sqrt{933} = 16.32$ lb/sec.

(f) $W_a = 16.32 - 800/3,600 = 16.1$ lb/sec.

(g) Ram drag $= M_a V = (16.1)(400)(1.467)/(32.2) = 294$ lb *ram drag*.

(h) $F = F_j - M_a V = 860 - 294 = 566$ lb *net thrust*.

If the jet velocity is desired, equation 18:21 may be solved:

(i) $V_j = (32.2)(860)/(16.32) = 1,697$ ft/sec.

18.7 General Remarks

At the present time, there is no standard thrust chart similar to a standard guaranteed power chart for a conventional engine. This is because altitude chambers equipped to handle such a large mass airflow have not been available in the past. However, by means of the engine characteristics outlined in section 18.5 it is possible to determine the effects of pressure and temperature on performance. Performance for a given engine can be corrected to standard conditions for that particular engine only.

Since individual engines of the same type will vary in thrust output over a range of some 10 to 12 per cent, airplane performance will depend upon the particular units used. In the future, standard thrust characteristics should be available and will be used in data analysis.

Thrust output of a unit deteriorates with service, falling off fairly rapidly during the first few hours and very gradually thereafter. Such factors as turbine blade erosion, tailpipe wall roughness from scale and service handling, tailpipe nozzle warpage, oil and dust accumulation on the impeller, and fuel nozzle distribution variation due to foreign matter will affect thrust. Flame tube deterioration probably has a minor effect.

Static thrust measurements should be made under carefully controlled conditions. Hot air in the vicinity of the burners should not be allowed to enter the compressor, such as would occur from a slight breeze if tested in the open. When tested in a chamber, the room may be sealed in order to measure the air consumption by means of a venturi entrance to the chamber. The unit will be exhausting outside the room, and the resulting pressure difference across the tailpipe area must be subtracted from the thrust scale reading.

Thrust may be measured at the engine mounts only without engine cowling. With the cowling in place, the compressor entrance pressure will be lower than atmospheric pressure, giving an additional pressure thrust on the engine. However, an equal drag force will exist on the cowling by virtue of the airflow, and the thrust measurement will be erroneous. Similarly, in flight, engine mount forces are greater than the propulsive thrust because of the interaction of air forces exerted between the two components. Flight tests have shown engine mount forces to be approximately equal to the jet thrust minus about three quarters of the ram drag in the P-59 installation. Such a thrustmeter would be useful only as a check on external changes to the airplane, which will not affect engine operation.

From the static thrust characteristics of the unit, the empirical variation in jet thrust for the individual variables is of the form:

$$F_2 = F_1 \left(\frac{N_2}{N_1}\right)^a \left(\frac{T_1}{T_2}\right)^{a/2} \left(\frac{P_2}{P_1}\right) \quad (18:53)$$

At the present time, this function is not useful, but in the future some such simple method of correcting thrust for all of the variables may be derived. In the present instance, the value of a is of the order of 3.5.

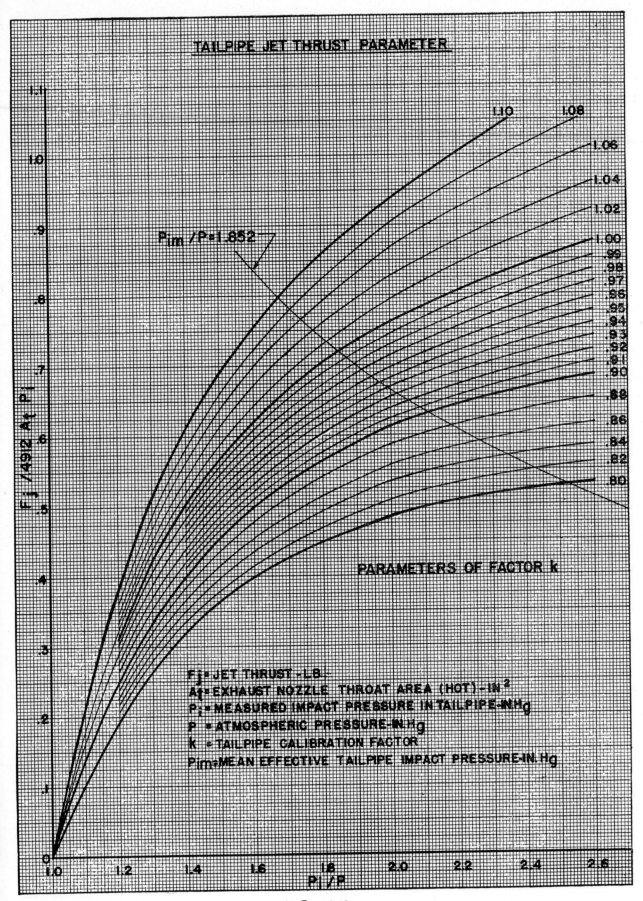

Fig. 18:12a

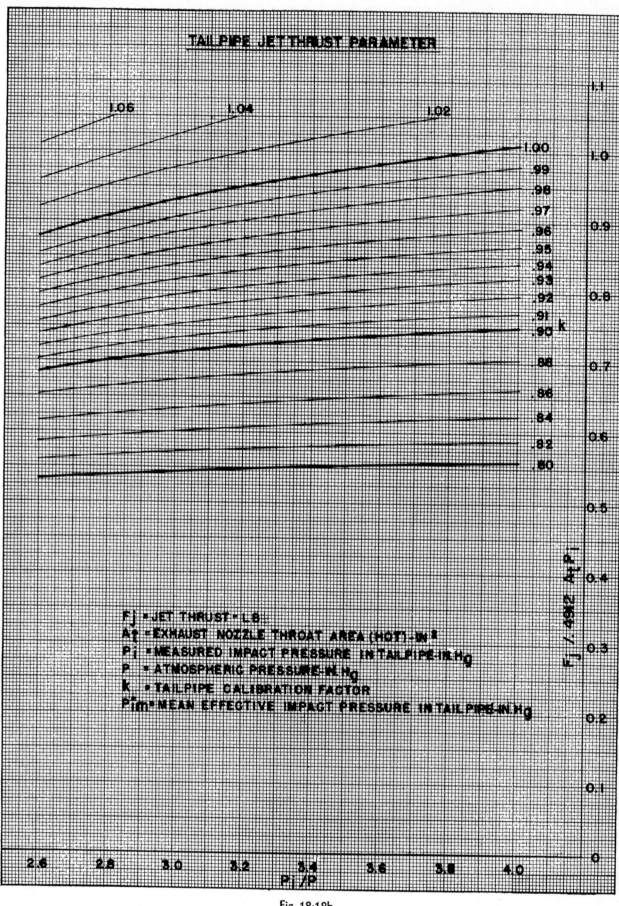

Fig. 18:12b

114

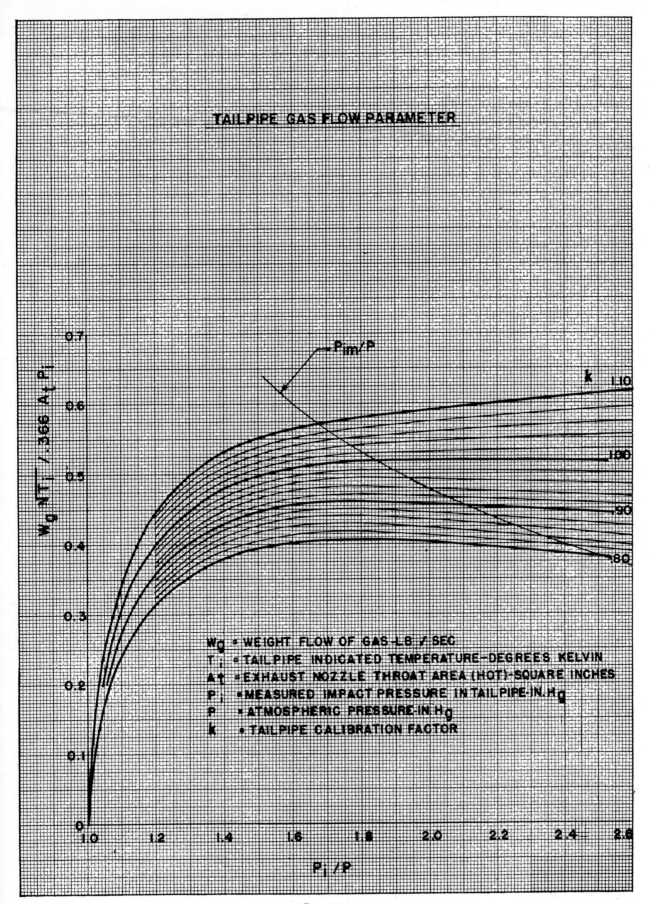

Fig. 18:13a

115

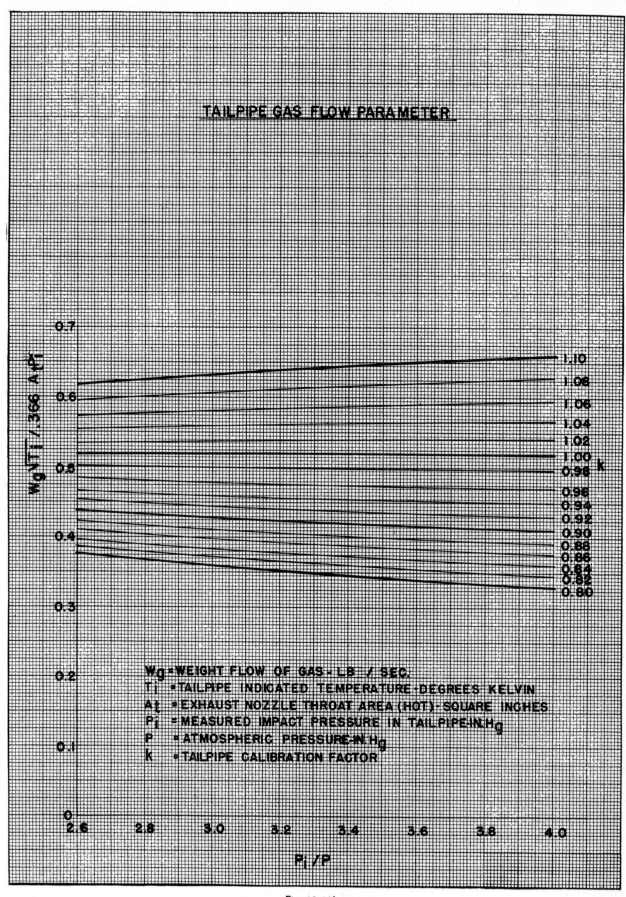

Fig. 18:13b

CHAPTER 19

CONCEPT OF THRUST AND DRAG

19.1 Definition of Forces Involved

Frequent discussions and arguments have centered around the definition of power plant thrust, its magnitude, where it acts, and the practicability of thrustmeters to measure it. Until thrust is defined, the term " airplane drag " has no significance. The following concept, based on reference 28, appears to be the most logical and fundamental.

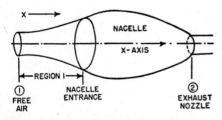

Fig. 19:1. Airflow through turbo-jet engine

Figure 19:1 represents the airflow handled by the turbo-jet engine and illustrates the terminology used.

Region 1: The streamline flow region from free air conditions to the nacelle entrance. (At station 1 static pressure is atmospheric.)

Region 2: Region 1 plus the nacelle interior.

Station 2: The exhaust nozzle, which is assumed to be exhausting to atmospheric pressure.

Nacelle interior: The region inside the nacelle through which the air passes including passages inside the engine.

Internal forces: The aerodynamic forces on the solid boundary of the *nacelle interior* (nacelle walls, engine, supports, and other internal surfaces).

External forces: Aerodynamic forces on the airplane other than the *internal forces.*

Pressure force: The normal component of aerodynamic forces on an area. *Viscous forces* are the tangential components. Only X-components are considered.

A_1: Cross-sectional area at station **1.**
A_t: Tailpipe exhaust nozzle area.
M_a: Mass flow of air past station **1.**
M_g: Mass flow of gases past station **2.**
P: Atmospheric pressure.
V: Free air velocity (at station 1).
S: X-component of resultant of all **pressure** and viscous forces exerted by the *nacelle interior* on the fluid passing through the nacelle. By the law of action and reaction the force of the fluid on the *nacelle interior* has the same **magnitude** but acts in the opposite direction.

X: X-component of resultant of all **forces** exerted by the outside air on the **streamline** boundary of " region 1."

From W. F. Durand (volume I[*]), we may **apply** the momentum theorem for steady flow to " region 2 " for unaccelerated flight conditions. This theorem states that the net change of momentum through the boundaries of " **region** 2 " equals the resultant of all *external forces* acting on the fluid inside this region or

$$F = M_g V_j - M_a V = S + X + P(A_1 - A_t)$$
$$(19:1)$$

Here the arbitrariness of defining thrust F by the momentum change is clearly evident, because the actual distribution of this thrust force is a complicated phenomenon. Actually the forces $X + P(A_1 - A_t)$ do not represent forces on the airplane, but it may be said that the airplane " eventually is influenced by these forces." This influence in reality acts as an *external pressure force* on the outer nacelle and wing surfaces as represented by the external flow of an ideal fluid, that is, no viscous forces.

19.2 Proof of Ideal External Pressure Force

For the reader's convenience the following proof of the previous statement is given. The reasoning

---

*Reference 25.

in W. F. Durand (volume IV, pages 185–187), is repeated below applied to the simple case of a single turbo-jet engine enclosed in a nacelle.

Imagine the nacelle placed in a large cylinder with its axis parallel to the X-axis and having a cross sectional area C. Consider the region bounded by the cylinder walls, the external boundary of "region 2," and two planes at stations 1 and 2. If conditions at station 1 are those of the undisturbed flow, the velocity at station 2 will be determined by the continuity equation $V(C - A_1) = V_2(C - A_t)$, and the pressure by Bernoulli's equation $P + \rho V^2/2 = P_2 + \rho V_2^2/2$. For this region the momentum equation is $\rho V(C - A_1)(V_2 - V) = E - X + P(C - A_1) - P_2(C - A_t)$, where E is the *external pressure force* on the nacelle for an ideal fluid. Using the equations for V_2 and P_2, the momentum equation reduces to:

$$E = X + P(A_1 - A_t) + \frac{\rho V^2}{2} \times \frac{(A_1 - A_t)^2}{(C - A_t)}$$

Thus in the limiting case where C tends toward infinity, the *external pressure force* on the nacelle reduces to $X + P(A_1 - A_t)$.

19.3 Definition of Thrust and Drag

Thrust may now be defined as the total *internal force* plus the ideal *external pressure force*.

Airplane *drag*, therefore, must be defined as the airplane profile drag (viscous external force) plus airplane form drag (actual external pressure force minus the ideal *external pressure force* determined by the operation of the unit) plus airplane induced drag. Notice that there is no attempt made to define any internal drag, nor to define the force on the actual engine. Thus a "thrust-meter," measuring engine mount forces, does not measure the airplane thrust as has been defined.

As commonly accepted, thrust is the rate of change of momentum (equation 18:17), but it may also be expressed as the force an airplane would experience if the *external* flow were perfect. Drag is, then, the resistance offered by a real fluid in the form of external viscous forces and deviation of the external pressure forces from the ideal distribution. One might object to the academic notion of a hypothetical pressure force. However, this notion is forced upon us if we desire to interpret the quantity $X + P(A_1 - A_t)$ as *a force on the airplane.*

19.4 Measurement of Drag in a Wind Tunnel

Consider the case of a power-off wind tunnel test of a complete model of a jet-propelled airplane. In determining the drag of the airplane for various flight conditions the *external* flow conditions should be reproduced. Internal airflow is irrelevant, although in order to produce the desired external flow, airflow into the nacelles at the correct velocity should be provided. Also, it should be possible to measure the momentum loss of air going through the nacelles. Obviously, the jet wake conditions cannot be simulated.

To obtain drag, we measure T = the total force on the airplane and L = the loss of momentum per unit of time of the air going through the nacelles $(MV - MV_e)$, where M = the mass flow of air through the nacelles, V = the tunnel velocity, and V_e = the nacelle exit velocity. Then $T - L$ = the drag as defined above.

This is so because T = the external viscous force plus the actual external pressure force plus the total internal force, and, as previously demonstrated, L = the total internal force plus the ideal *external pressure force*. Notice that the reasoning is independent of the interpretation of $X + P(A_1 - A_t)$. All the quantities in this expression depend solely upon the external flow, which was supposed to be the same in flight as in the tunnel test.

GLIDE POLARS

20.1 Purpose

Because of the large drag of airplane propellers, determination of the lift-drag coefficient polar from power-off glide tests for conventional airplanes would have little significance. It is practically impossible to make accurate corrections for removing the propeller effects from such a polar, and the slipstream is a further source of difficulty. In the case of jet-propelled airplanes, a better opportunity of evaluating the basic airplane characteristics is afforded.

This chapter deals with the determination of the total airplane resistance during glide tests, and this resistance is here referred to as drag. From the foregoing chapter it is realized that this " drag " value has a limited significance, but this method is outlined in order that it may be extended to the attractive possibilities of future applications when a method of accounting for the internal airflows is developed. Proper internal airflows should be controlled during the glide, perhaps by providing an adjustable nacelle exit at the rear. Measurement of airflow through the engine may be developed from " windmilling " data and ground tests, at various rpm, of the air consumption resulting from motoring the engine over by means of external power. At any rate, the airplane drag results at the proper nacelle inlet velocities should be corrected for the momentum change of the internal airflow as indicated in section 19.4.

Actual glide polar results, without considering internal airflow, have yielded reasonable values of airplane drag coefficients and span efficiency factors. However, further development of this technique is indicated, and information much more reliable than that obtained from wind tunnel tests should be realized in the future.

Essentially, the method is to climb to altitude and shut off the power plants. During descent at constant observed airspeed, data may be taken

from which the glide angle is determined. Weighing the airplane after landing provides accurate weight data for calculating the lift and drag characteristics.

20.2 Method

The forces acting on an airplane in a power-off glide are represented in Figure 20:1. The lift and drag are the only two forces available to balance the gross weight vectorially for equilibrium conditions. Their magnitudes and directions depend entirely on the glide path angle θ.

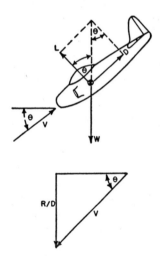

Fig. 20:1.   Forces acting during glide

Rate of descent and true speed along the flight path determine the glide angle. During steady glide the rate of change of pressure altitude is converted into tapeline rate of descent by the free air temperature ratio exactly as in the case of climb. (See section 14.3.)

$$R/D = \frac{dH_p}{dt} \frac{T}{T_s} = \text{ft/min} \qquad (20:1)$$

True airspeed is determined in the normal manner, but the airspeed system should be dynamically balanced to avoid errors caused by the rate of change of pressure altitude (see section 5.31) and:

$$\theta = \sin^{-1} \frac{R/D}{88\,V} \qquad (20:2)$$

Lift and drag depend on the gross weight and glide angle:

$$L = W \cos\theta \qquad (20:3)$$

$$D = W \sin\theta \qquad (20:4)$$

The lift and drag coefficients are calculated by

$$C_L = \frac{391\,L}{\sigma S V^2} \qquad (20:5)$$

$$C_D = \frac{391\,D}{\sigma S V^2} \qquad (20:6)$$

The C_L versus C_D polar may be plotted, and C_D may be plotted versus $C_L{}^2$ from the slope of which the span efficiency factor, used as the square root of Oswald's factor, may be calculated from equation 12:4 copied as:

$$e = \left[\frac{(\Delta C_L)^2}{\pi R (\Delta C_D)} \right]^{1/2} \qquad (20:7)$$

The effect of flaps, landing gear, or other variable components may be found by repeating glide polars for these conditions.

It will be found difficult to obtain accurate results for high speed glides, so several repetitive runs should be made. Usually two or three polar points may be obtained during one glide, but possible Mach number or Reynolds number effects should be anticipated. It would be best to obtain all data at the same altitude, but experience will dictate judicious technique. If fuel quantity can be accurately determined in flight a series of sawteeth may be made by starting the engine and climbing back to the original altitude, noting the fuel quantity for each run. Fuel readings should all be taken at one observed airspeed in level flight, for which attitude an accurate calibration of the fuel quantity gages should be made available.

20.3 Data Reduction and Data Required

Data reduction for one glide point is illustrated in Table 16. Airplane configuration must be carefully recorded.

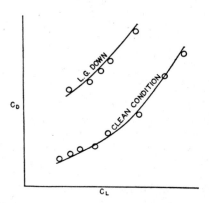

Fig. 20:2. Airplane lift-drag coefficient polar

Plots of all test points will appear as illustrated in Figures 20:2 and 20:3 from which C_{Dp} and e may be obtained. The parasite drag coefficient is the drag coefficient at zero lift coefficient from extrapolation of the straight line portion of the curve.

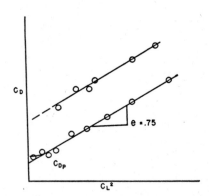

Fig. 20:3. Lift-drag polar replotted versus lift coefficient squared

TABLE 16. DETERMINATION OF LIFT AND DRAG COEFFICIENTS — DATA REDUCTION

1*	H_{pr}	ft	20,300	Altitude chosen from glide data.
2*	V_r	mph	206	Observed airspeed.
3*	t_r	°C	−28	Observed free air temperature.
4	V_m	mph	208	(2) − lab. inst. cal. error.
5	V_{cal}	mph	199.5	(4) − position error for (4).
6	H_{pm}	ft	20,250	(1) − lab. inst. cal. error.
7	H_p	ft	20,025	(6) − position error for (4) and (6).
8	M	—	.383	Figure 8:1b for (5) and (7).
9	$M\sqrt{K}$	—	.332	K for free air pickup = .75 here.
10	t_m	°C	−30	(3) − lab. inst. cal. error.
11	t	°C	−35	Figure 8:2a for (9) and (10).
12	V_c	mph	691	Figure 8:2a for (11).
13	V	mph	265	(8) × (12).
14	σ	—	.555	Figure 8:3c for (7) and (11).
15	dH_p/dt	ft/min	1,495	Slope of H_{pr} vs. time at (1).
16	t_s	°C	−25	Standard from Figure 8:3c for (7).
17	T/T_s	—	.96	[(11) + 273]/[(16) + 273].
18	R/D	ft/min	1,435	(15) × (17).
19	$\sin\theta$	—	.0615	(18)/88 × (13),
20	θ	deg	3.52	$\sin^{-1}$ .0615.
21*	W	lb	9600	Observed gross weight.
22	L	lb	9575	(21) cos (20).
23	D	lb	590	(21) × (19).
24	S	ft²	400	Wing area.
25	C_L	—	.24	391 × (22)/(14) × (24) × (13)².
26	$C_L{}^2$	—	.0573	(25)².
27	C_D	—	.0148	391 × (23)/(14) × (24) × (13)².

*Flight test data required.

CHAPTER 21

MAXIMUM SPEED DETERMINATION

21.1 Discussion

In analyzing jet propulsion performance, brake horsepower becomes an indefinite quantity in that it is directly dependent upon true airspeed. Therefore, it becomes more logical and much simpler to work with airplane drag and propulsive thrust available.

Level flight speeds for jet propulsion require a longer time to reach stabilization than for a conventional airplane as may be seen from the figure. That is, there is less excess thrust available for acceleration to the equilibrium speed. Consequently, speed runs should be run for approximately five minutes. As indicated in Figure 21:1 the thrust available in the high-speed ranges is approximately constant, while for a propeller, it decreases with increase in speed.

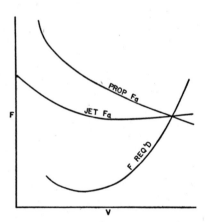

Fig. 21:1. Comparison of propeller and turbo-jet thrust available versus velocity

Since there is no standard thrust performance for jet propulsion engines and since the output varies between units, all performance should be obtained with the same power plant. This is because correction to standard conditions applies only to the specific engines for which the data are obtained. If air has to pass over airplane surfaces before entering the nacelle, these surfaces must be carefully inspected for smoothness and continuity as their condition may have a large effect on compressor entrance conditions and therefore thrust output.

Because of the freedom from vibration, it will be found necessary to install a buzzer on the altimeter to eliminate friction in the instrument during level flight runs.

21.2 Method

Evaluating thrust requires some labor, and since there is no standard or guaranteed thrust for flight conditions, it is not too important in determining maximum speed performance. However, since thrust is a function of altitude, speed, rpm, and temperature, we can use the appropriate parameters and correct our results to standard by these parameters. By dimensional analysis and empirical results net thrust available is found to be expressed by a function of the following parameters (see equation 18:15):

$$\frac{F}{P} = f\left(\frac{V}{\sqrt{T}}, \frac{N}{\sqrt{T}}\right) \qquad (21:1)$$

The thrust required for level flight at standard gross weight will be equal to the airplane drag, which may be obtained by multiplying equation 12:1 by $375/V$:

$$D = C_9(V\sqrt{\sigma})^2 + \frac{C_{10}}{(V\sqrt{\sigma})^2} \qquad (21:2)$$

where

$$C_9 = C_{D_p}S/391$$
$$C_{10} = 124.6(W_s/ekb)^2$$

Substituting the expression for σ, equation 2:5, and rearranging, the expression for the ratio of airplane drag to atmospheric pressure is:

$$\frac{D}{P} = C_{11}\left(\frac{V}{\sqrt{T}}\right)^2 + \frac{C_{12}}{P^2\left(\frac{V}{\sqrt{T}}\right)^2} \qquad (21:3)$$

where

$$C_{11} = \frac{C_9 T_0}{P_0}$$

$$C_{12} = \frac{C_{10} P_0}{T_0}$$

Equation 21:1 expressed the thrust available parameter in terms of the speed and rpm parameters independently of the atmospheric pressure. In equation 21:3 the airplane drag parameter depends upon the speed parameter but is also dependent upon the atmospheric pressure. However, these two equations may be set equal to each other for level flight equilibrium conditions for a constant atmospheric pressure and gross weight.

$$f\left(\frac{V}{\sqrt{T}}, \frac{N}{\sqrt{T}}\right) = f\left(\frac{V}{\sqrt{T}}\right) \quad \text{at constant } P \quad (21:4)$$

This means that a curve of $N/\sqrt{T}$ versus $V/\sqrt{T}$ may be plotted from test data for a series of speed runs, by varying the rpm of the engine at a constant pressure altitude, provided we correct the speeds for gross weight variation (section 21.3). It will be found that this plot is a straight line (except for compressibility effects)

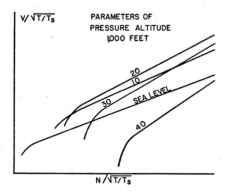

Fig. 21:2. Standard speed-rpm polars for level flight

for the airplane speed range above the speed for minimum drag. As shown in the figure, a family of such polars will result for various pressure altitudes attributable to the effect of pressure noted in equation 21:3, neglecting T_s in these parameters for the moment.

For standard performance at any given rpm, it would merely be necessary to calculate $N/\sqrt{T_s}$, enter this curve, read $V\sqrt{T_s}$, and multiply the latter by $\sqrt{T_s}$. The result would give the standard

airplane speed at the desired rpm for standard temperature at the test pressure altitude. In other words, maximum speed performance has been reduced to standard conditions at a standard density altitude equal to the pressure altitude for which the test data are obtained. This process is greatly simplified by plotting the parameters shown in Figure 21:2 in the first place. The resultant curve then reads directly in terms of rpm and mph for standard altitude parameters equal to the pressure altitudes of test.

The speed and rpm parameters shown in Figure 21:2 are, therefore, standard values and are denoted by N_s and V_s.

Reading standard maximum speeds for the desired engine rpm at each altitude gives the final desired speed performance versus altitude

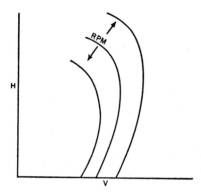

Fig. 21:3. Level flight speed performance versus altitude

shown in Figure 21:3. Note that there is no well-defined critical altitude. Since the engine itself has no critical altitude, the altitude at which maximum speed obtains depends entirely on the particular airplane characteristics. For a given engine, airplane performance for different types of airplanes will have no common characteristics.

Since it has been shown above that either $V/\sqrt{T}$ or $N/\sqrt{T}$ uniquely determines the other for steady level flight conditions at a *constant pressure altitude*, then it follows that the following are complete functions also. These relations are useful for more detailed analysis purposes.

$$\frac{V}{\sqrt{T}} = f\left(\frac{N}{\sqrt{T}}\right) \quad \text{or} \quad V_s = fN_s$$

$$F \text{ or } F_j = f\left(\frac{N}{\sqrt{T}}\right) = f\left(\frac{V}{\sqrt{T}}\right) = f(V\sqrt{\sigma})$$

$$= fN_s = fV_s$$

21.3 Gross Weight Correction

It has been previously noted that in the higher speed ranges the net propulsive thrust varies little with true airspeed. Consequently, correcting a level flight airspeed for a change in gross weight, assuming the thrust to remain *constant*, will be accurate within experimental error. This assumption will be used to adjust all speed test results to correspond to a common standard gross weight, these resulting speed values then being used to plot the speed-thrust polar of the preceding section.

For level flight, equation 21:2 may be equated to the thrust available, and then it may be solved for equivalent airspeed at standard gross weight:

$$V\sqrt{\sigma} = \sqrt{\frac{F + \sqrt{F^2 - 4\,C_9 C_{10}}}{2\,C_9}} \qquad (21{:}5)$$

If R is assumed to be the ratio of the actual to the standard gross weight, W/W_s, then the equivalent airspeed for any gross weight would be expressed by equation 21:5 with R^2 appearing in the term involving C_{10}. Defining the correction factor C_F as being the ratio of these speeds for standard and actual gross weights:

$$C_F = \frac{V\sqrt{\sigma} \text{ at } W_s}{V\sqrt{\sigma} \text{ at } W} \quad \text{for constant } F \qquad (21{:}6)$$

The actual solution of this equation reduced to its simplest form becomes

$$C_F = \sqrt{\frac{1 + \sqrt{1 - C_{13}/F^2}}{1 + \sqrt{1 - C_{13}R^2/F^2}}} \qquad (21{:}7)$$

where

$$C_{13} = \frac{4\,C_{D_p}S}{\pi}\left(\frac{W_s}{ekb}\right)^2$$

This correction factor, then, depends upon the magnitude of the thrust, which in turn may be calculated by equation 21:2 for standard gross weight and any equivalent airspeed. Therefore, for any given equivalent airspeed the correction factor may be calculated for a series of gross weight ratios. This process may be carried out for any specific airplane, and a plot similar to that in Figure 21:4 may be obtained.

Although somewhat laborious, once this curve has been derived it becomes very useful. For jet-propelled airplanes a weight correction to speed becomes very important because of the large gross weight variation caused by fuel consumption, some 20 per cent or more, and the high operational altitudes. In order to keep this correction factor to a minimum, slow speed points should be run first, when the minimum amount of fuel has been consumed. Minor changes in configuration, or errors in establishing e and C_{D_p} will not alter the factor appreciably since most of the speed corrections will be of the order of ½ to to 3 per cent in speed.

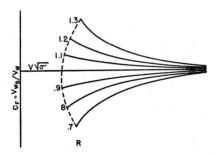

Fig. 21:4. Airspeed correction factor for gross weight variation

It is desirable to establish a standard gross weight versus altitude as a basis of all performance reduction, as it is impossible to fly at a high altitude at design or take-off gross weight, which would be an unnecessary penalty to impose. Engine fuel consumption curves may be used in estimating the gross weight variation during flight, or fuel flowmeters may be used.

21.4 Universal Speed-Thrust Polar

If thrust during flight is determined, another method of maximum speed analysis is possible.

Equation 21:2 may be written for any gross weight in level flight

$$F = C_9\,(V\sqrt{\sigma})^2 + \frac{C_{10}R^2}{(V\sqrt{\sigma})^2} \qquad (21{:}8)$$

If this equation is divided by $R = W/W_s$

$$F_w = C_9(V_w\sqrt{\sigma})^2 + \frac{C_{10}}{(V_w\sqrt{\sigma})^2} \qquad (21{:}9)$$

where

$$F_w = \frac{F}{(W/W_s)}$$

$$V_w\sqrt{\sigma} = \frac{V\sqrt{\sigma}}{\sqrt{W/W_s}}$$

If thrust, true speed, and gross weight are obtained, then F_w can be plotted against $V_w\sqrt{\sigma}$.

For standard gross weight the weight ratio is 1.0 and this universal thrust-speed polar automatically reduces the speed results to standard weight conditions. Except for Mach or Reynolds number effects, this curve will be valid for any altitude as shown in Fig. 21:5. Actually, slightly different

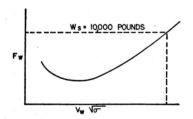

Fig. 21:5.   Universal thrust-speed polar

curves have resulted from flight tests at different altitudes showing reduced performance with increasing altitude. This is probably caused by the effect of Reynolds number variation or drag coefficient. Mach number effects will be revealed as a steepening of the curve slope at the higher speeds.

If this method is used, then standard thrust must be known before standard $V\sqrt{\sigma}$ can be read from the polar. This can be found for the particular engine by plotting the F/P versus $N/\sqrt{T/T_s}$, and the standard thrust computed from the value for the standard rpm. (See Figure 21:6.)

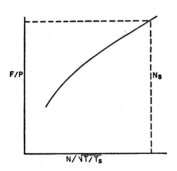

Fig. 21:6.   Net thrust parameter versus standard rpm

21.5 Alternate Universal Method

It has been found possible to take flight test speed run data for a given airplane and reduce all of the test data to a single universal curve by use of a special parameter. Such a plot completely describes all level flight speed performance, above speeds for minimum thrust, and can be used to determine speed versus altitude curves for any desired engine operating speeds.

The full significance of this result is not under-

stood completely at the present time, but is given here for future study. Essentially the procedure is as follows:

(a) Plot $N/\sqrt{T}$ versus $V\sqrt{\sigma}$ for the various pressure altitudes.

(b) Plot $N/\sqrt{T}$ versus P on log-log paper for parameters of $V\sqrt{\sigma}$ selected from (a).

(c) Determine the average slope m of the curves from (b) such that $N/\sqrt{T} = KP^m$.

(d) Plot $NP^{-m}/\sqrt{T}$ versus $V\sqrt{\sigma}$ as in Figure 21:7.

Data plotted in this form have been found to give a remarkably straight line. Departures from the straight line represent the approach to the

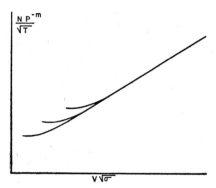

Fig. 21:7.   Universal rpm-speed polar

minimum drag regions at the various altitudes and are not of particular interest. For some airplanes values of the exponent, $(-m)$, have been found to be of the order of .25, using degrees Kelvin, inches of mercury, rpm, and mph.

21.6 Data Reduction and Data Required

The calculations in Table 17 represent the data reduction for one speed run. At least five speed runs should be made, and rpm values for the runs should be selected for the given airplane. No runs should be made at speeds less than 110 percent of the speed for minimum drag. At low altitudes, a wide range of engine speeds may be used, but at higher altitudes, higher engine speeds at smaller increments must be chosen.

Below the speed for minimum drag, a stabilized speed cannot be obtained because such a condition is unstable. At speeds near that for minimum drag the gross weight correction will be large. Also, flight data at altitude at low gross weight and low speed cannot be used since it will be found that the airplane is flying above its absolute

TABLE 17. TYPICAL SPEED RUN — DATA REDUCTION

1*	H_{pr}	ft	20,120	Observed pressure altitude.
2*	V_r	mph	280	Observed airspeed.
3*	t_r	°C	−29	Observed free air temperature.
4	t_m	°C	−30	(3) − lab. inst. cal. error.
5	V_m	mph	282	(2) − lab. inst. cal. error.
6	V_{cal}	mph	276	(5) − position error for (5).
7	H_{pm}	ft	20,240	(1) − lab. inst. cal. error.
8	H_p	ft	20,015	(7) − position error for (7) and (5).
9	$V\sqrt{\sigma}$	mph	271	(6) − compressibility correction from Figure 4:2.
10	M	—	.527	Figure 8:1c for (6) and (8).
11	$M\sqrt{K}$	—	.457	Using $K = .75$ for temperature pickup.
12	t	°C	−39.5	Figure 8:2a for (4) and (11).
13	V_c	mph	685	Figure 8:2a for (12).
14	V	mph	361	(13) × (10).
15*	W	lb	8,500	From plot of W versus time or fuel consumed.
16	R	—	.85	(15)/(W_s = 10,000 lb.)
17	C_F	—	.985	For (9) and (16): see sect. 21.3.
18	V at W_s	mph	356	(14) × (17) = V at W_s at constant F.
19	t_s	°C	−25	Standard temperature from Figure 8:3c for (8).
20	$\sqrt{T/T_s}$	—	.971	[(12) + 273]/[(19) + 273].
21	V_s	mph	362	(18)/(20).
22*	N_r	1/min	15,800	Observed rpm.
23	N_m	1/min	15,850	(22) − lab. inst. cal. error.
24	N_s	1/min	16,120	(23)/(20).

*Flight test data required.

ceiling for standard weight at the same thrust conditions.

Thus at a standard gross weight of 10,000 pounds at a standard density altitude of 20,015, the airplane will do 362 mph employing 16,120 rpm. When all the test points are plotted, standard level flight speed for any rpm may be read from the curve.

CHAPTER 22

CLIMB PERFORMANCE

22.1 Discussion

Referring to Figure 22:1 of power available and that required for level flight, the difference in climb characteristics between conventional and jet-propelled airplanes may be noted. Maximum rate of climb occurs at the speed at which the slopes of the power available and required curves

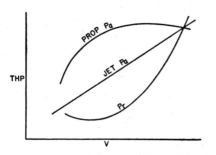

Fig. 22:1. Comparison of propeller and jet thrust horsepower available

are equal. Obviously, the jet-propelled airplane will obtain its maximum climb performance at a considerably higher airspeed. For conventional, high-powered airplanes best climbing speed will be in the vicinity of 50 to 55 per cent of maximum level flight speed. In the case of jet propulsion, this value is of the order of 75 to 80 per cent. Thus the climb angle for jet propulsion will be very small compared to conventional flight paths. This means that a much larger distance will be covered during climb, a tactical advantage, and that climb computations may safely neglect climb angle corrections. Furthermore, the troublesome slipstream is absent, and drag-producing cooling gadgets are nonexistent.

It is apparent from Figure 22:1 that rate of climb versus airspeed will have an appreciably flatter slope at its maximum value. This requires more saw-tooth points to define best climbing speed accurately, but also an appreciable variation in climbing speed will have very little effect on rate of climb.

In the figure, power plants are so chosen that this airplane has the same maximum speed at this altitude with either. Note the superior performance of the conventional airplane in all other respects. However, if the jet-propulsion engine static thrust, at zero velocity, is increased to that value for the conventional engine-propeller combination, then the former will have vastly superior performance in all respects.

22.2 Method

In this case, exactly the same density altitude method for climb reduction outlined in Chapter 14 is used. Here, however, the problem of correcting to standard thrust is much simpler than the previous correction to standard power. The correction to climb for gross weight remains the same.

As before, rate of change of pressure altitude is corrected to tapeline rate of climb by correcting to standard temperature at the test pressure altitude (equation 14:13). Actual rate of climb at the actual density altitude is then known.

It is desired to correct to standard conditions at the same atmospheric density, implying constant equivalent and true airspeeds. Standard density altitude will be determined by standard atmospheric pressure and temperature, differing from both the actual pressure and temperature but resulting in the same density altitude. Pressure and temperature each affect thrust output differently. (See section 18.7.)

In section 18.5, it was shown how net propulsive thrust may be determined from the engine manufacturer's parameter curves. Calculation of actual thrust, correcting pressure and temperature to engine inlet conditions and including airspeed effects, and then recalculation to obtain net thrust under the standard pressure and temperature conditions would be very laborious. The difference between these two values would be the difference in excess thrust for climb since the thrust required for level flight is identical in both instances. It has been found by experience that the difference between actual and standard gross jet thrust, assuming atmospheric conditions at the compressor inlet, will yield practically the same increment, certainly well within experimental errors. All that is desired is the net effect of the pressure and temperature changes on thrust, and this simple procedure applies very nicely to rate of climb reduction.

The increment in excess thrust by the simple method in correcting to standard density condition is

$$\Delta F_e = \left(\frac{F_{j_s}}{P_s}\right) P_s - \left(\frac{F_j}{P}\right) P = F_{j_s} - F_j \quad (22:1)$$

where F_{j_s}/P_s is read from the engine curve for $N_s\sqrt{T_s}$ and F_j/P for $N/\sqrt{T}$ of test, both at an entrance pressure ratio of one, no ram conditions.

Then, by equation 14:1, the rate-of-climb increment will be

$$(\Delta R/C)_1 = \frac{88 \, \Delta F_e V}{W} \quad (22:2)$$

and, as before, equation 14:16:

$$(R/C)_1 = (R/C) + (\Delta R/C)_1 \quad (22:3)$$

The correction to rate of climb for gross weight is identical to that derived in section 14.3, equations 14:19 and 14:20:

$$(\Delta R/C)_2 = -(R/C)_1 \frac{\Delta W}{W} \quad (22:4)$$

$$(\Delta R/C)_3 = -C_8 \frac{\Delta W}{V\sigma} \quad (22:5)$$

where

$$C_8 = \frac{21,930}{(ekb)^2}$$

Section 22.4 gives a detailed illustrative example of this method.

22.3 Universal Rate-of-Climb-Speed Curves

Again a universal relationship for plotting climb performance may be derived for the jet-propelled airplane similar to that in section 14.2. It is included here for future consideration.

Equation 21:8 may be written and equated to thrust available by adding the excess thrust for climb term from equation 14:1:

$$F = C_9(V\sqrt{\sigma})^2 + \frac{C_{10}R^2}{(V\sqrt{\sigma})^2} + \frac{RW_s(R/C)\sqrt{\sigma}}{88 \, V\sqrt{\sigma}} \quad (22:6)$$

This expresses the thrust available or required for any gross weight. Solving for $(R/C)\sqrt{\sigma}$ and dividing by the square root of the weight ratio gives

$$R_w\sqrt{\sigma} = \frac{88 \, V_w\sqrt{\sigma}}{W_s}\left[F_w - C_9(V_w\sqrt{\sigma})^2 - \frac{C_{10}}{(V_w\sqrt{\sigma})^2}\right] \quad (22:7)$$

where

$$R_w\sqrt{\sigma} = \frac{(R/C)\sqrt{\sigma}}{\sqrt{W/W_s}}$$

$$V_w\sqrt{\sigma} = \frac{V\sqrt{\sigma}}{\sqrt{W/W_s}}$$

$$F_w = \frac{F}{(W/W_s)}$$

Note the similarity to equation 14:8, where the power terms in the latter have been converted into thrust by the factor $V_w\sqrt{\sigma}/375$.

Thus for a constant thrust parameter in equation 22:7, the rate-of-climb parameter may be plotted against the speed parameter. The family

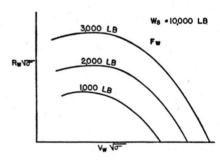

Fig. 22:2. Universal rate-of-climb-speed curves

of curves is presented in Figure 22:2, from which any climb information for any flight conditions may be obtained. Flight tests could not be made at a constant value of the thrust parameter, but the results could be properly faired.

22.4 Data Reduction and Data Required

The same remarks and notes found in section 14.4 apply here with the exception of refer-

TABLE 18. RATE OF CLIMB — DATA REDUCTION

1*	H_{pr}	ft	25,000	Observed data: selected values.
2*	t_r	min	26.5	Observed data: from (1) vs. (2) at (1).
3	H_{pm}	ft	25,100	(1) — lab. inst. cal. error.
4	H_p	ft	24,930	(3) — position error for (7) and (3).
5	dH_p/dt	ft/min	2,400	Slope of (1) versus (2) at (1).
6*	V_r	mph	210	Observed data: at (1).
7	V_m	mph	208	(6) — lab. inst. cal. error.
8	V_{cal}	mph	203	(7) — position error for (7).
9	M	—	.429	Figure 8:1b for (8) and (4).
10	$M\sqrt{K}$	—	.429	Use $K = 1.0$ for total temperature pickup.
11*	t_r	°C	−45	Observed data: at (1).
12	t_m	°C	−48	(11) — lab. inst. cal. error.
13	t	°C	−56	Figure 8:2a for (10) and (12).
14	V_c	mph	661	Figure 8:2a for (13).
15	V	mph	284	(9) × (14).
16	σ	—	.495	Figure 8:3c for (13) and (4).
17	H_D	ft	22,200	Figure 8:3c for (16).
18	t_s	°C	−34.5	Standard free air temperature from Figure 8:3c for (4).
19	T/T_s	—	.91	[(13) + 273]/[(18) + 273].
20	R/C	ft/min	2,185	(5) × (19): eq. 14:13.
21*	N_r	1/min	16,480	Observed data: at (1).
22	N_m	1/min	16,430	(21) — lab. inst. cal. error.
23	t	°F	−69	See (13): engine manufacturers still use °F, Figure 25:1a.
24	t_{sd}	°F	−20	Standard temperature for (17): Figures 8:3c and 25:1a.
25	P	lb/in.²	5.47	For (4): ref. 1.
26	P_s	lb/in.²	6.15	For (17): ref. 1.
27	N_s	1/min	16,500	Rated rpm.
28	$N/\sqrt{T}$	—	830	$(22)/\sqrt{(23) + 460}$.
29	$N_s/\sqrt{T_{sd}}$	—	786	$(27)/\sqrt{(24) + 460}$.
30	F_i/P	in.²	194]	From F/P versus $N/\sqrt{T}$ engine curve for (28).
31	$(F_i/P)_s$	in.²	159	From F/P versus $N/\sqrt{T}$ engine curve for (29).
32	F_i	lb	1,061	(30) × (25).
33	F_{is}	lb	978	(31) × (26).
34	ΔF_e	lb	−83	(33) − (32).
35	$2\Delta F_e$	lb	−166	For two-engine airplane (same rpm).
36*	W	lb	9,500	From W versus time for saw tooth.
37	$(\Delta R/C)_1$	ft/min	−436	88 × (35) × (15)/(36): eq. 22:2.
38	$(R/C)_1$	ft/min	1,749	(20) + (37).
39	W_s	lb	10,000	Standard gross weight.
40	ΔW	lb	500	(39) − (36).
41	$(\Delta R/C)_2$	ft/min	−92	−(38) × (40)/(36): eq. 22:4.
42	$(\Delta R/C)_3$	ft/min	−45	$-(C_s) \times (40)/(15) \times (16)$: eq. 22:5.
43	$(R/C)_s$	ft/min	1,612	(38) + (41) + (42).

*Flight test data required.

ence to horsepower. Otherwise, a sample set of calculations is illustrated in Table 18.

An actual rate of climb of 2,185 ft per minute was obtained at a density altitude of 22,200 ft at 9,500 lb gross weight employing 16,430 rpm.

Under standard conditions of 22,200 ft density altitude, 10,000 lb gross weight, and 16,500 rpm, standard rate of climb is 1,612 ft per minute.

In computing C_8 a value of the square root of Oswald's span efficiency factor = .837 and a wing span of 50 ft was used.

Note that in correcting rate of change of pressure altitude to actual rate of climb, standard temperature for the test pressure altitude is used (items 18, 19, and 20 and equation 2:4). This rate of climb actually occurs at a given density, item 16, which is determined by the test pressure alti-

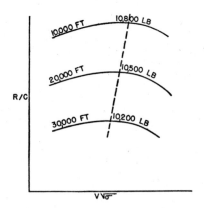

Fig. 22:3. Rate of climb versus equivalent airspeed

tude and temperature. Reference to Figure 8:3c reveals that neither the atmospheric pressure nor temperature represent standard conditions. However, for this same density, the density altitude, which is the altitude at which this density would occur in a standard atmosphere, may be read from the same figure, item 17 of the table. Keeping the density constant will not alter the aerodynamic forces on the airplane, but the new pressure and temperature values, items 26 and 24, will affect the engine thrust, which is corrected accordingly and is illustrated in the table.

These calculations are complete for saw-tooth reduction. For climb to ceiling, items 16 and 39–43 may be omitted, item 38 being the standard rate of climb at standard density altitude equal to item 17.

Characteristic saw-tooth and climb-to-ceiling results are illustrated by Figures 22:3 and 22:4.

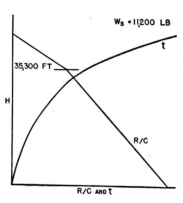

Fig. 22:4. Rate-of-climb performance

CHAPTER 23

TAKE-OFF AND LANDING

23.1 Ground Run Distance

The method used is identical to that for the conventional airplane as given in section 15.2. In determining the increment of thrust in going to standard rpm, pressure, and temperature conditions it will be sufficiently accurate merely to evaluate the static thrusts.

$$\Delta F_s = \Delta F_0 + (F_{j_s} - F_j) \qquad (23:1)$$

Equation 15:9 is then used exactly as before, and is copied here for reference:

$$S_s = S_0 \left(\frac{W_s}{W}\right)^2 \left(\frac{\Delta F_0}{\Delta F_s - \mu \Delta W}\right)\left(\frac{\sigma}{\sigma_s}\right) \qquad (23:2)$$

It will usually be found that landing flap deflection will reduce the take-off run sufficiently to warrant its use, and this effect should be investigated. At present the ratio of static thrust to gross weight is lower than for conventional airplanes, resulting in a somewhat longer ground run. Also, since the flaps are not affected by slipstream, there will not be this added drag penalty caused by high slipstream velocities.

In order to improve take-off performance three methods of augmenting the thrust of a turbo-jet engine are being studied. One method involves the injection of a relatively large quantity of a water-alcohol mixture into the compressor inlet. Lower compressor inlet temperatures result in increased mass airflow, while the water reduces combustion chamber temperatures sufficiently to permit the burning of the extra fuel with the excess oxygen. A marked thrust gain results at the expense of considerable liquid consumption.

Another method, referred to as afterburning, involves the injection of additional fuel into the tailpipe aft of the turbine, which in essence amounts to a ramjet engine in series with a turbo-jet. Such a system involves additional complication and results in a relatively high fuel consumption in order to realize a considerable thrust boost.

A third scheme is to rob compressor discharge air and pipe it to an auxiliary combustion chamber and nozzle, where additional fuel is introduced and burned, the system somewhat resembling a ramjet in parallel with a turbo-jet. Water is then introduced in the combustion chamber, providing steam to rectify the unbalanced mass flow created between compressor and turbine. Again a very considerable thrust increase is realized, but with an alarming liquid consumption when considered for a protracted period of time.

Probably the most practical take-off assistance for general use will be provided by auxiliary, solid-propellant rockets providing a high thrust for a limited duration. These auxiliary rockets may be jettisoned after take-off so that the airplane performance will in no way be compromised by the take-off assistance problem.

23.2 Air-Borne Distance

Again the same principles used in section 15.3 may be followed in deriving a general expression for air-borne distance. It is simple to convert the power terms to thrust terms in equation 15:20. Multiplying and dividing the numerator by $V/375$ and the denominator by $V_s/375$, where $V_s = V(\sigma/\sigma_s)^{.5}(W_s/W)^{.5}$.

$$S_s = S_0 \left(\frac{W_s}{W}\right)^{1.5} \left(\frac{\sigma}{\sigma_s}\right)^{.5} \frac{V}{V_s}\left[\frac{F_e}{F_s - (F - F_e)W_s/W}\right] \qquad (23:3)$$

or

$$S_s = S_0 \frac{W_s}{W}\left[\frac{F_e}{F_s - (F - F_e)W_s/W}\right] \qquad (23:4)$$

TABLE 19. TAKE-OFF DISTANCE — DATA REDUCTION

			GROUND-RUN DISTANCE		
1*	S	ft	1,700	Average observed ground run.	
2*	V_g	mph	95	Average take-off ground speed.	
3*	V_w	mph	5	Wind velocity runway component.	
4	V_0	mph	100	(2) + (3): eq. 15:2.	
5	S_0	ft	1,862	(1) × [(4)/(2)]$^{1.85}$: eq. 15:1.	
6	a_0	ft/sec²	5.76	(1.075) × (4)²/(5): eq. 15:4.	
7*	W	lb	10,700	Average take-off gross weight.	
8	ΔF_0	lb	1,915	(7) × (6)/g: eq. 15:5.	
9*	H_p	ft	2,200	Average pressure altitude.	
10*	t	°C	33	Observed.	
11	σ	—	.861	Figure 8:3a for (9) and (10).	
12	t	°F	91	Converted to °F system for engine data.	
13	P	lb/in.²	13.58	Corresponding to (9): ref. 1.	
14	t_s	°F	59	Standard sea level conditions.	
15	P_s	lb/in.²	14.7	Standard sea level conditions.	
16*	N_r	1/min	16,500	Average rpm.	
17	N_m	1/min	16,450	(16) − lab. inst. cal. error.	
18	N_s	1/min	16,500	Standard rating.	
19	$N\sqrt{T}$	—	700	(17)/$\sqrt{(12)+460}$.	
20	$(N/\sqrt{T})_s$	—	724	(18)/$\sqrt{(14)+460}$.	
21	F_j/P	in.²	110	From engine curve for (19).	
22	$(F_j/P)_s$	in.²	124	From engine curve for (20).	
23	F_{j_s}	lb	1,822	(22) × (15).	
24	F_j	lb	1,494	(21) × (13).	
25	ΔF_j	lb	328	(23) − (24).	
26	$2\,\Delta F_j$	lb	656	Twin-engine airplane.	
27	ΔF_s	lb	2,571	(8) + (26).	
28	W_s	lb	11,000	Standard gross weight.	
29	ΔW	lb	300	(28) − (7).	
30	$\mu\Delta W$	lb	12	.04 × (29) for hard turf.	
31	S_s	ft	1,265	Eq. 23:2.	
			AIR-BORNE DISTANCE		
32*	H	ft	50	Obstacle height.	
33*	t	sec	4.5	Time from take-off to obstacle.	
34*	S	ft	1,340	Observed data.	
35	S_0	ft	1,373	(34) + 1.467 (3) × (33): eq. 15:10.	
36	R/C	ft/min	667	60 × (32)/(33): eq. 15:14.	
37	av V	mph	208	Approx. = (35)/1.467 × (33).	
38	F_e	lb	390	(7) × (36)/88 × (37): eq. 23:6.	
39	$2\,F_{j_s}$	lb	3,644	2 × (23): two engines.	
40	$2\,F_j$	lb	2,988	2 × (24): two engines.	
41	$2\,F_j - F_e$	lb	2,598	(40) − (38).	
42	W_s/W	—	1.028	(28)/(7).	
43	S_s	ft	566	Eq. 23:5.	
			TOTAL DISTANCE		
44	S_s	ft	1831	(31) + (43)	

*Flight test data required.

Since actual and net thrust calculations are laborious and the improvement in accuracy is of questionable value, jet thrust values will be used.

$$S_s = S_0 \frac{W_s}{W}\left[\frac{F_e}{F_{j_s} - (F_j - F_e)W_s/W}\right] \qquad (23:5)$$

where:

$$F_e = \frac{W(R/C)}{88\,V} \qquad (23:6)$$

23.3 Landing Roll Distance

Equation 15:22 remains unaltered:

$$S_s = S\left(\frac{V_g + V_w}{V_g}\right)^{1.85}\left(\frac{W_s}{W}\right)\left(\frac{\sigma}{\sigma_s}\right) \qquad (23:7)$$

23.4 Data Reduction and Data Required

Data from a number of take-off tests should be averaged and reduced to standard as illustrated in Table 19. All variables should be kept reasonably constant.

CHAPTER 24

RANGE AND ENDURANCE

24.1 Discussion

The primary variables affecting the range of the jet-propelled airplane are altitude, rpm, airspeed, and gross weight. Of these four, altitude is by far the most important. At 40,000 ft economical range may be 300 to 400 per cent of that at sea level. It is desirable, from a fuel economy standpoint, to fly at or above critical altitude for maximum speed, although pilot comfort, oxygen supply, and other factors may limit the practical altitude to some lower value.

Considerably less flight testing for range data is necessary for the jet-propelled airplane because only one airspeed at a given rpm is possible at a given altitude. By varying both rpm and manifold pressure, the conventional airplane speed may be kept constant, thus necessitating investigation of power conditions. For this case speed-rpm polars, N_s versus V_s, must be determined for several altitudes and at least two gross weights. Fortunately, fuel consumption may be plotted in a parameter form which is practically independent of altitude and gross weight. Combining these two types of curves will give range and endurance under any desired operating conditions in a manner similar to the method outlined in Chapter 16.

Maximum range will be found to occur at considerably higher speeds than for the conventional airplane because the efficiency of this type of propulsion increases with speed.

24.2 Method

Fuel consumption from the engine manufacturer's parameter curves at zero airspeed, no ram condition, are shown in Figure 24:1. It has been found by experience that all fuel consumption data in level flight at all altitudes when atmospheric temperature and pressure values are used will plot very nearly on one curve. The mathematical relationship has not as yet been

determined, but the effects of ram are not great, and flight test data include these effects. If data from climb are plotted, a separate curve slightly

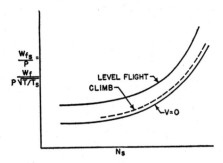

Fig. 24:1. Standard fuel flow parameter characteristics

above that for zero ram will be found. Fuel consumption data should be taken at two widely different altitudes to substantiate the fuel consumption parameter curve.

Airplane level flight polars (Figure 24:2) should be obtained down to as near the speed for minimum thrust, or drag, as possible. It is best to

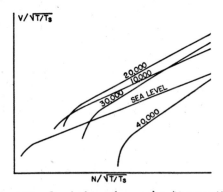

Fig. 24:2. Standard speed-rpm polars (V_s versus N_s)

obtain all flight data in the low-speed range at a slightly higher gross weight than standard. Otherwise, at the lower speeds it will be found that the flight conditions may exceed the corresponding ceiling conditions for standard gross weight. It will be necessary to make recalculations and plots of the speed correction factor for gross weight (section 21.3) for the desired standard weights. Generally, two gross weights should be sufficient, one near full load gross weight and one near weight empty by means of changing ballast.

Having evaluated these fuel consumption and speed-polar curves, they may be combined mathematically to give the relation between miles per pound of fuel consumed and airspeed. For a given altitude, weight, and rpm, select fuel consumption and speed parameters from the curves. In the case of the polar the standard airspeed is read directly for the standard rpm. Likewise, the fuel consumption parameter is read for this rpm. Then miles per pound is calculated by

$$\frac{V}{W_f} = \frac{V_s/P}{W_{f_s}/P} = \text{mi/lb} \qquad (24:1)$$

where W_f = lb fuel/hour for all engines.

Plotting the miles per pound versus speed curves for all altitudes and gross weights results

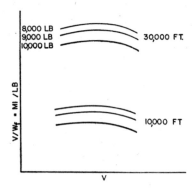

Fig. 24:3.   Miles per pound of fuel versus true airspeed

in curves shown in Figure 24:3. If maximum range is desired, the peak miles per pound values may be chosen and plotted against gross weight. The

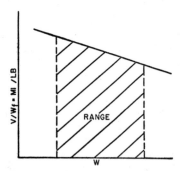

Fig. 24:4.   Miles per pound of fuel versus gross weight

area under the curve for gross weights with full fuel and no fuel will be the range as shown in Figure 24:4.

Endurance for any conditions is easily determined by evaluating W_f, pounds of fuel per hour, versus airspeed. If $1/W_f$ is plotted against gross weight, the area will be endurance in hours.

Operating conditions are very simple to define. A single curve of rpm versus altitude for optimum range is all that is needed for practical purposes. Fuel consumption versus time may be determined if desired. In case of multi-engine aircraft, range data should be obtained with one or more engines inoperative. Maximum range will usually occur at full rpm for minimum number of engines. That is, at low altitudes single-engine range for a twin-engine airplane may easily be 20 per cent greater than that for twin-engine operation at the same altitude.

Fuel consumed during climb should be determined by means of the fuel consumption and time to climb curves. Because of the high airspeed for climb, the distance traveled while ascending should also be evaluated. Fuel consumed versus altitude will be very close to a straight line, as the fuel consumption rate decreases with altitude approximately as does the rate of climb. (See Figure 24:5.) Most economical climb will be found to occur at maximum allowable rpm.

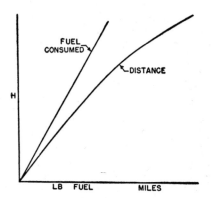

Fig. 24:5.   Fuel consumed and distance traveled during climb

Finally, economical range or range at maximum speed may be presented as shown in Figure 24:6. If glide distances are desired the glide polar data given in Chapter 20 may be used.

Head and tail winds should be considered. Going back to the miles per pound versus speed curves, the ground speed will be changed directly by the algebraic addition of the wind velocity. Miles per pound are then multiplied by the ratio of the new to the original ground speed for each point. These new curves may be carried through to the evaluation of range in determining the effect of wind.

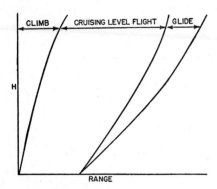

Fig. 24:6. Range versus altitude

24.3 Data Reduction

An outline of the general steps is indicated here. Specific examples are not given because data reduction will vary depending upon circumstances and preferences. All fundamental analysis such as true speed determination is covered in previous chapters.

Flight test data:

(a) Determine values of W, V, N, H_p, t, W_f.

(b) Correct V to V_w, for actual to standard gross weight.

(c) Plot $W_f/P\sqrt{T/T_s}$ versus $N/\sqrt{T/T_s}$.

(d) Plot $N/\sqrt{T/T_s}$ versus $V/\sqrt{T/T_s}$, where standard density altitude is equal to the test pressure altitude. Speed and rpm parameters then become standard values.

Calculations:

(e) Combine plots of (c) and (d) to obtain pounds per mile versus V_s by equation 24:1. Repeat for each gross weight and altitude test condition.

(f) For range plot pounds per mile versus gross weight and determine area under curve corresponding to fuel weight. This may be done for constant speed, constant rpm, or optimum range condition.

(g) For endurance plot the reciprocal of the fuel consumption versus gross weight and take the area under the curve corresponding to the fuel load.

FLIGHT TEST REPORT OUTLINE

In order to standardize the form of reporting experimental flight test results, a memorandum to serve as a guide for preparing such reports is given here for reference purposes. This outline is based upon reference 31 and on N.A.C.A. *Technical Reports*. It is sufficiently comprehensive to provide the basic structure for any report of an experimental, developmental, or investigative nature. It is not intended that all reports embody all of these elements, but only that the general structure and order of presentation of the material be adhered to. The extent and completeness of any report is dictated by the purpose for which it is intended and the results achieved.

I. PREFACE

1. Title Page.
2. Table of Contents.
   (a) Table of contents.
   (b) List of figures (and photographs).
   (c) List of tables.
3. Summary.
   (a) Character and result of investigation (tabular results whenever possible).
   (b) Brief recommendations.

II. TEXT

1. Introduction.
   (a) Reason, authority, or cause for initiation of investigation.
   (b) Object, purpose, aim.
   (c) Definition: explanation of terms, list of symbols.
   (d) Importance, significance or utility of investigation.
   (e) History: survey of progress with mention of references.
   (f) Scope: range of the study, limitations.
2. Apparatus (Test Equipment).
   (a) Description of subject, material, or object used for the investigation. Include photograph if possible (airplane configuration, for instance).
   (b) Description of special test equipment or instrumentation used in the investigation.
3. Procedure.
   (a) Theory: Brief explanation of principles involved or premises and assumptions accepted.
   (b) Method of conducting test.
   (c) Method of reduction and analysis of data.
   (d) Results: presentation of and discussion of, final curves or tabulated results.
4. Conclusion.
   (a) Brief and general enumeration of facts established, validity and value of results (success achieved).
   (b) Suggestions and recommendations.

III. APPENDIX

1. Derivation of theory, theoretical investigations, formulas.
2. Tables of computations and data.
3. Figures and charts used and developed in analysis.
4. Instrument calibration curves, supplementary curves, and charts.
5. Log of operations (flights), that is, flight numbers, changes made, subject of test, results, personnel, test time, total time, and so on.
6. List of references (bibliography).

Thus the report embodies three fundamentals, namely the *preface*, the *text*, and the *appendix*.

In the preface the title page affords a glance at the material and the writer (or the source of the information) and will be noted by 98 per cent of those who pick up the report.

The table of contents presents a topical outline indicating the substance of the main divisions.

Of the whole report the greatest emphasis is placed on the *summary*, which 85 per cent of those who look at the report will read. After reading the summary the reader will either ignore the report, circular file it, bury it in his library, be interested or curious enough to investigate further, or accept the results as valid and be guided by them in future discussions and decisions. Since only about 20 per cent of the readers will peruse the treatise beyond this point, it is of the utmost importance that the summary reflect the full portent, significance, and weight of the diligence involved. Remember that many people will be too preoccupied with other important work to devote the time to study the report. It is for these persons particularly that the summary is embodied, and for this reason the whole report will often be scored according to the summary alone. *The best means of presenting a summary of results is by means of a table or graph studiously selected and composed to achieve brevity.* One picture is worth a thousand words and a sketch is worth hundreds of them.

The *text* provides a complete, relatively general explanation and understanding of the methods and materials employed and the success of achievement of the complete program. This serves as a basis of evaluating the thoroughness and validity of the work performed. Note that the final results are incorporated in the text, but that all of the details which represent most of the *labor* involved are screened from the general but complete treatise by the *appendix*. The appendix provides the substance upon which progress thrives through the diligent efforts of the student, the research worker, and the person who performs the work, while the remainder of the treatise is designed to publish and disseminate the fruits of the efforts. Thus the text is not encumbered with lesser details.

An *appendix* is a supplement. It is supplementary to the text. An *addendum* is an addition. It adds new information to a previously completed report.

When the context of the report is complex, that is, maximum speed investigation, climb determination, take-off determination, and so on, the appendices I, II, III, etc., should be so subdivided. Addendums are to be discouraged. If subsequent testing warrants reporting, it should merit a report of its own with reference to a previous report. In the new report this outline should still be followed, but repetition of description, methods, and so on, may be eliminated by referring to the previous reports, which is one of the reasons for providing a list of references.

The results of any investigation, however significant and momentous, are useless until the engineer who has achieved such results can express them clearly and completely to the uninitiated. Mastery of language and grammatical accuracy is a prerequisite of a successful engineer.

This outline should be a guide and not a tyrant. Every writer should be Captain of his course. However, all reports should be as homogeneous as possible for maximum efficiency of preparation and utility. Reports are the best means of others for judging the character of your work.

REFERENCES

1. DIEHL, W. S.: Standard Atmosphere — Tables and Data. Washington: N.A.C.A. Technical Report 218, 1925.
2. WILDHACK, W. A.: Pressure Drop in Aircraft Instrument Installations. Washington: N.A.C.A. Technical Note 593, 1937.
3. WALCHNER, O.: The Effect of Compressibility on the Pressure Reading of a Prandtl Pitot Tube at Subsonic Flow Velocity. Washington: N.A.C.A. Technical Memorandum 917, 1939.
4. BEIJ, K. H.: Aircraft Speed Instruments. Washington: N.A.C.A. Technical Report 420, 1941.
5. GLAUERT, H.: The Elements of Airfoil and Airscrew Theory. England: Cambridge University Press, 1926.
6. PRANDTL, L., and TIETJENS, O. G.: Applied Hydro- and Aeromechanics. New York: McGraw-Hill Book Company, 1934.
7. SCHOOLFIELD, W. C.: A Simple Method of Applying the Compressibility Correction in the Determination of True Airspeed. Journal of the Aeronautical Sciences, October, 1942; vol. 9, pages 457–464.
8. COLMAN, P.: Temperature Effects on Turbine Supercharger Installations. Journal of the Aeronautical Sciences, October, 1943; vol. 10, pages 261–269.
9. Recommended Test Procedure for Aircraft Engine Turbo Supercharger Power Plants. Washington: N.A.C.A. Advance Restricted Report 3F22, June, 1943.
10. DIEHL, W. S.: The Calculation of Take-Off Run. Washington: N.A.C.A. Technical Report 450, 1933.
11. HARTMAN, E. P.: Consideration of the Take-Off Problem: Washington: N.A.C.A. Technical Note 557, 1936.
12. Hamilton Standard Method of Propeller Performance Calculation. East Hartford, Conn.: Propeller Division, United Aircraft Corporation.
13. Airplane Climb Performance. Washington: C.A.A Flight Engineering Report 3.
14. REED, A. C.: Airplane Performance Testing at Altitude. Journal of the Aeronautical Sciences, February, 1941; vol. 8, pages 135–150.
15. Nomenclature for Aeronautics. Washington: N.A.C.A. Technical Report 474, 1941.
16. von KARMAN, T.: Compressibility Effects in Aerodynamics. Journal of the Aeronautical Sciences, July, 1941; vol. 8, pages 337–356.
17. CAMERON, D.: Note on the Effect of Position Error on Compressibility Correction. England, Boscombe Down: Report No. A and AEE/Res/ 147, May 15, 1941.
18. THOMPSON, F. L., and ZALOVCIK, J. A.: Airspeed Measurements in Flight at High Speeds, Washington: N.A.C.A. Advance Restricted Report, October, 1942.
19. CROSBY, F. M.: A Simplified Method of Brake Horsepower Correction. Niagara Falls, N. Y.: Bell Aircraft Report 02–923–036, February 28, 1944.
20. BIKLE, P. F.: Performance Flight Testing Methods in Use by the Flight Section. Washington: Army Air Forces Technical Report 5069, January 15, 1944.
21. WETMORE, J. W.: The Rolling Friction of Several Airplane Wheels on Tires and the Effect of Rolling Friction on Take-Off. Washington: N.A.C.A. Technical Report 583, 1937.
22. Stability and Control Requirements for Airplanes. Washington: Army Air Forces Specification C-1815.
23. Procedure for Testing of Aircraft. Washington: Army-Navy Aeronautical Specification AN-T-40.
24. GILRUTH, R. R.: Requirements for Satisfactory Flying Qualities of Airplanes. Washington: N.A.C.A. Confidential Report, April, 1941.
25. DURAND, W. F., Editor: Aerodynamic Theory. Pasadena: Durand Reprinting Committee, California Institute of Technology.
26. WELMERS, E. T.: Universal Flight Test Analysis for Whittle Jet Propulsion. Niagara Falls, N. Y.: Bell Aircraft Report 02–923–041, August 8, 1944.
27. BRIDGMAN, P. W.: Dimensional Analysis. New Haven, Conn.: Yale University Press, 1931.
28. LAGERSTROM, P. A.: Concepts of Thrust and Drag for a Jet-Propelled Airplane. Niagara Falls, N. Y.: Bell Aircraft Aerodynamics Research Note 8, December 29, 1944.
29. ZAHM, A. F.: Pressure of Air on Coming to Rest from Various Speeds. Washington: N.A.C.A. Technical Report 247, 1926.
30. LAGERSTROM, P. A.: Application of Dimensional Analysis to Jet Engines and Jet-Propelled Airplanes. Niagara Falls, N. Y.: Bell Aircraft Aerodynamics Research Note 11, March 26, 1945.
31. BAKER, R. P.: The Preparation of Reports: Scientific, Engineering, Administrative, Business. New York: Ronald Press Company, 1938.

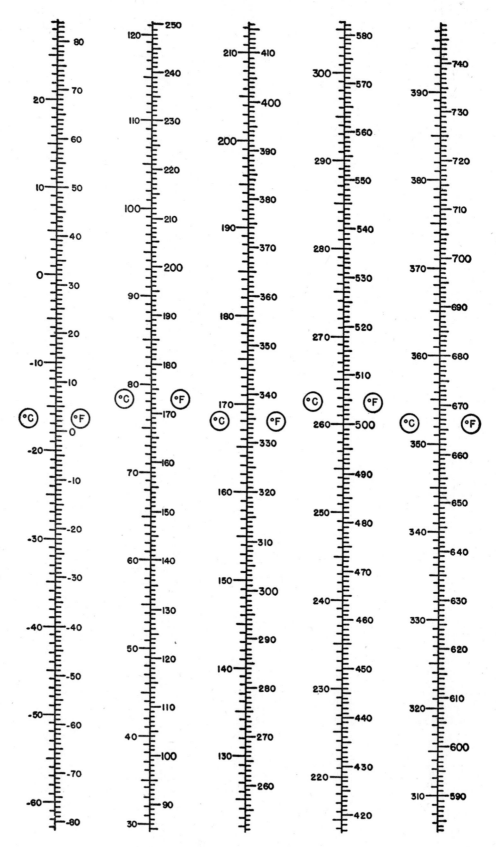

Fig. 25:1a. Centigrade-Fahrenheit Conversion Scales

140

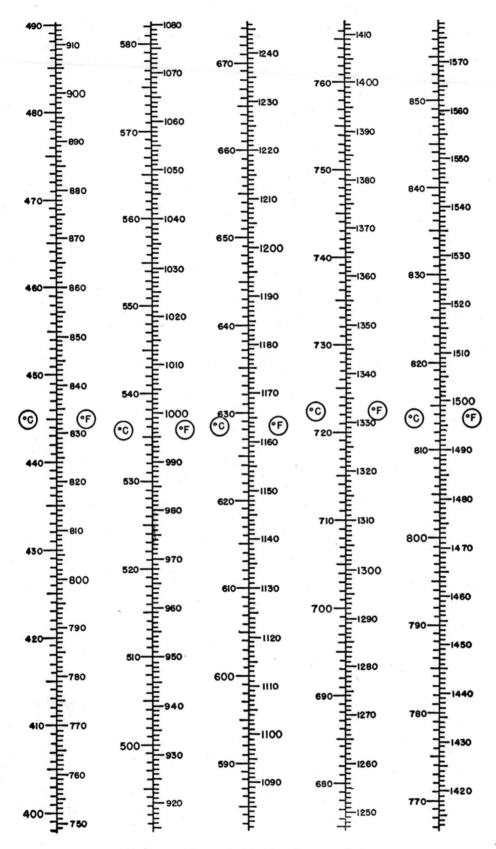

Fig. 25:1b. Centigrade-Fahrenheit Conversion Scales

141

INDEX

Acceleration effect on instruments, 26
Adiabatic compression, 6
Adiabatic temperature rise, 29
Airflow — see engine characteristics
Airspeed (also see standard notation)
    Calibration airspeed, 11
    Compressibility correction, 11
    Compressibility increment curves, 12
    Equivalent airspeed, 11
    Stalling speed, 43
    True airspeed, 32
Airspeed calibration — see airspeed position error
    determination
Airspeed head
    Compressible flow theory, 6, 10
    Incompressible flow theory, 5
    Typical head calibrations, 13
Airspeed indicator, 10
Airspeed measurement errors
    Acceleration, 13, 14, 26
    Compressibility correction, 11–14
    Dynamic unbalance, 13, 14
    Instrument laboratory calibration, 4, 13
    Position error, 13, 14
Airspeed position error
    Definition, 14
    Effect of altitude, 19, 24, 25
    Effect of gross weight, 23, 24
    Effect of Mach number, 25
    Pressure equivalent charts, 17, 18
Airspeed position error determination
    Altimeter method, 15–20
    Pacing method, 23
    Speed course method, 20, 21
    Trailing bomb method, 22, 23
Altimeter position error, 15–20
Altimeter vibration, 122
Altitude
    Absolute, 3
    Correction for temperature, 3
    Density, 3
    Density altitude charts, 40–42
    Pressure, 3, 15
    Tape line, 3
Altitude — effect on
    Airspeed position error, 19, 24, 25

Engine power, 45–47
Atmosphere
    Density ratio, 4, 29
    Density ratio charts, 40–42
    Pressure variation, 3

Bernoulli's equation
    Compressible flow, 6, 10
    General, 5
    Incompressible flow, 5, 6
Brake mean effective pressure, 48

Calibration airspeed, 11
    Variation with Mach number, 33–37
Carburetor air temperature, 4
    Effect of fuel vaporization, 55
    Effect on BHP, 47, 51, 52, 55, 58
Carburetor air temperature rise, 58
Center of gravity
    Effect on stalling speed, 44
Centrifuge, 26
Climb, 69–77
    Angle, 69, 70
    Correction for power, 73, 74
    Correction for weight, 74
    Data required, 75
    Engine power correction to standard, **73**
    Equation, 69, 71
    Example of data reduction, 76
    Forces acting, 69
    Lag in pressure instruments, 77
    Sawteeth, 70
    Temperature correction to observed rate of
        climb, 72
    Time to climb, 75
    Universal method, 72
    Wind velocity gradient effect, **71**
Climb — jet airplanes, 127–130
    Best climbing speed, 127, 130
    Correction for gross weight, 128
    Correction for thrust, 127, 128
    Data reduction, 129
    Data required, 129
    Method, 127
    Universal curves, 128
    Universal equation, 128

Compressible flow theory, 6, 10
Compressibility
  Airspeed correction, 11–13
  Critical airflow, 7–9
  Shock wave, 7–9
Compression ratio for superchargers, 52–55
  Charts for variation with temperature, 53, 54, 56
  Effect of fuel vaporization, 55
Compressor entrance conditions, 104
Configuration chart, 68
Control — see stability
Control surfaces — various types of, 89, 90
Conversion chart for temperatures, 140, 141
Critical altitude, 51–57
  Data reduction, 58, 59
  Data required, 59
  Definition, 51
Critical altitude — jet airplanes, 123
Critical Mach number, 8, 9
Critical pressure, 8, 9
Critical tailpipe pressure ratio, 108

Density — effect on
  Engine power, 46
  Power required, 60
  Take off distance, 80, 81
Density ratio — atmospheric, 4, 29
  Charts, 40–42
Differential pressure, 7, 10
Dimensional analysis of turbo-jet engine
  Compressor entrance conditions, 104
  General functions, 104
  Parameters depending upon airspeed, 105
  Parameters independent of airspeed, 104
  Sample solution, 104
  Universal performance plot, 105
  Variables involved, 103, 104
Dives — effect of Mach number, 95
Drag
  Definition, 118
  Glide test measurement, 119, 120
  In level flight, 122
  Wind tunnel measurement, 118
Dynamic balance of airspeed system, 14, 22
Dynamic pressure, 6, 11

Endurance — see range
Engine characteristics — turbo jet engines
  Airflow, 106, 107
  Composite performance presentation, 107
  Effect of atmospheric pressure on thrust, 112
  Effect of atmospheric temperature on thrust, 112
  Effect of rpm on thrust, 112
  Entrance conditions, 106
  Fuelflow, 107

Jet thrust, 106
Net thrust, 106
Net thrust variation with airspeed, 107
Service effects, 112
Static thrust measurements, 112
Tailpipe temperature, 107
Tailpipe thrust — see thrust
Engine power
  Altitude variation, 45–47
  Best power, 50
  Climb standard power, 73
  Correction to standard conditions, 51, 52, 55, 58, 59
  Correction to standard for climb, 73, 74
  Determination from power charts, 47
  Economical power, 50
  Excess power for climb, 72
  Factor, 46
  Maximum speed standard power, 64
  Mixture effect, 50
  Ram effect, 51
  Supercharging effects, 48–50
  Temperature variation, 47
  Variables affecting power, 50
Engine power curves
  Determination of chart BHP, 47
  Theory of power curves, 45
  Types of, 48, 49
  Use of power curves, 47
Equivalent airspeed, 11, 25

Fin — see stability — directional
Fin stall, 98
Flight test program, 1
Free air temperature
  Adiabatic temperature rise, 29
  Along a streamline, 29
  Determination of — example, 30
  Effect of Mach number, 29, 38, 39
  Graphical determination of, 31, 38, 39
  Pickup calibration, 30
  Pickups, 28
  Recovery factor, 29
  Standard altitude variation, 40–42
Free air temperature determination
  Charts, 38, 39
  Data reduction, 30, 31
  Data required, 30, 31
Fuel — cooling effect on air intake, 55
Fuelflow — see engine characteristics
Full throttle power correction, 51, 52, 58, 59

Gas constant for air, 6, 8
Gas constant for exhaust gases, 108
Glide tests
  Angle, 119, 120

Glide tests—*Continued*
    Data required, 121
    Forces acting, 119
    Polars, 119, 120
    Rate of descent, 119
    Sample calculations, 121
Gross weight
    Effect on airspeed, 61, 66
    Effect on airspeed position error, 23, 24
    Effect on power required, 61
    Effect on range & endurance, 84, 85
    Effect on rate of climb, 72, 74
    Effect on take off distance, 80, 81
    Variation during flight, 44
Gross weight — jet airplanes
    Effect on level flight speeds, 124
    Effect on rate of climb, 128

Impact pressure, 11
Incompressible flow theory, 5
Instrument calibration error, 4

Jet propulsion
    Advantages, 102, 103
    Engine cycle, 103
    Fuel air ratio, 103
    Limitations, 103
    Propulsive efficiency, 102

Lag in airspeed system, 14
Landing distance, 81
Landing roll distance — jet airplanes, 132
Level flight — jet airplanes
    Power required, 127
    Thrust required, 122, 124
Lift coefficient, 25
    Maximum, 44

Mach number, 7, 8
    Charts, 33–37
    Critical, 8, 9
    Definition, 8, 27
    Equation, 27
    Theoretical derivation, 27
Mach number — effect on
    Airspeed position error, 25
    Measured free air temperature, 29, 38, 39
    Pitching moment, 95
    Pressure coefficient, 8, 9
Manifold pressure
    Altitude variation, 45–47
    Correction to standard, 57
    Effect on BHP, 55
    Temperature effect chart, 53, 54
Maximum lift coefficient, 44

Effect of center of gravity location, 44
Maximum speed determination, 64–67
    Example of data reduction, 67
    Gross weight correction, 66
Maximum speed determination — jet airplanes, 122–126
    Correction for gross weight, **124**
    Critical altitude, 123
    Data reduction, 125, 126
    Data required, 126
    Reynolds number effect, 125
    Rpm-speed polars, 123
    Temperature correction, 123
    Thrust required & available, 122
Mixture — effect on power, 50
Momentum reaction of tailpipe gases, 106
Momentum theorem, 117

Nacelle external forces, 117, 118
Nacelle internal forces, 117
Nernst cycle, 103
Notation, see book covers
Nozzles — flow in, 7, 8
    Critical pressure, 8
    Density at throat, 8
    Velocity of sound in throat, 8

Operating conditions for maximum range, **85**
Outline for writing reports, 137, 138

Pitot-static tube, 6, 10, 13
Position error — see airspeed or altimeter
Power — see engine power
Power — jet airplanes
    Required and available for level flight, **127**
Power coefficient — propeller, 61
Power required
    Climb, 74
    Level flight, 60
    Universal equation, 61
Pressure
    Altitude variation, 15
    At compressor entrance, 106
    Position error equivalent, 17, 18
    Rate of variation with altitude curves, **16**
Pressure coefficient, 8, 9
    Variation with Mach number, 9
Pressure distribution, 9, 14
Propeller — destabilizing effect, 98
    Power coefficient, 61
Propulsive efficiency — jet airplanes, **102**

Range and endurance, 83–86
    Data reduction, 86
    Data required, 86

Range and endurance—*Continued*
    Determination of, 84, 85
    Engine characteristics, 83
    Gross weight effect, 84, 85
    Miles per pound of fuel, 84
    Operating chart, 85
    Radius of action, 85
    Wind effects, 85
Range and endurance — jet airplanes, 133–135
    Data reduction, 135
    Discussion, 133
    Economical climb, 134
    Effect of gross weight, 134
    Fuel consumption, 133
    Miles per pound of fuel, 134
    Pilot's operating conditions, 134
    Rpm-speed polars, 133
References, 139
Report outline, 137
Rudder — see stability-directional
Rudder stall, 98

Schedule of flight testing, 1
Shakedown flight tests, 1
Sound, velocity of, 7, 8, 29
Span-efficiency factor, 60
Specific fuel consumption, 50
Speed course — airspeed calibration, 20, 21
Speed for best climb, 70
Speed-power polar, 66
Stability and control — directional
    Fin stall, 98
    Rudder fixed, 98
    Rudder free, 98
    Rudder stall, 98
    Snaking, 98
Stability and control — general
    Flight conditions, 88
    General, 87, 90, 91
    Preliminary flight tests, 91
    Requirements, 88, 89
    Types of control surfaces, 89, 90
    Types of stability, 87, 88
Stability and control — lateral
    Adverse yaw, 99
    Rate of roll, 99, 100
    Stick force limitation, 99, 100
    Stick free, 99
    Structural limitation, 100
    Wing tip helix angle, 99, 100
Stability and control — longitudinal
    Accelerated flight
        CG neutral point, 96
        Effect of altitude, 95
        Mach number effects, 95, 96

        Stick fixed, 94
        Stick free, 94, 95
    Forward CG limitations, 95
    Linear flight
        CG neutral point, 96
        Effect of bob weight, 93
        Effect of CG location, 92
        Effect of springs, 93
        Effect of stabilizer incidence, 93
        Stick fixed, 92
        Stick free, 93
        Trim tab effectiveness, 94
    Theoretical considerations, 97
Stalling speed, 43, 44
    Data reduction, 43, 44
    Data required, 44
    Variables, 43
Static pressure position error curves, 17, 18
    see airspeed position error
Streamline flow, 5
    Equation of motion, 5
    Variation of temperature, 29
    Variation with velocity, 7
Supercharger
    Calculations, 57
    Compression ratio curves, 53, 54
    Effect of fuel vaporization, 55
    Theory, 52–57
Supersonic flow, 7, 8
Symbols, see end papers

Take-off distance
    Air-borne distance method, 80, 81
    Air-borne wind correction, 80
    Alternate obstacle distance method, 81
    Correction to standard, 80, 81
    Data required, 81
    Ground run method, 78–80
    Sample calculations, 76
    Wind correction, 78, 79
Take-off distance — jet airplanes
    Air-borne distance, 131
    Data reduction, 132
    Data required, 132
    Ground run, 131
Temperature
    Adiabatic rise in stopped airflow, 29
    Calculation of exponent n, 57
    Carburetor air, 4
    Carburetor air temperature rise, 58
    Chart for determining free air values, 38, 39
    Conversion chart, 140, 141
    Correction to observed rate of climb, 72
    Effect of fuel vaporization, 55
    Exponent n for power correction, 52, 55, 56

Temperature—*Continued*
  Free air temperature determination, 28–31
  Variation along a streamline, 29
  Variation with velocity, 29
Temperature — effect on
  BHP, 47, 52
  Observed rate of climb, 72
  Supercharger compression ratio, 53, 54, 56
  Velocity of sound, 7, 29, 38, 39
Temperature — jet airplanes
  Centigrade-Fahrenheit conversion chart, 140, 141
  Correction for level flight speeds, 123
  Effect on engine thrust, 112
  Rise at compressor entrance, 106
Thrust — jet airplanes
  Available, 107, 122
  Concept of, 117, 118
  Definition, 117, 118
  In climb, 128
  Required, 122
  Standard thrust, 124, 125
Thrust determination by tailpipe method
  Airflow for sonic flow, 110
  Airflow for subsonic flow, 109, 110
  Calibration factor, 110, 111
  Critical pressure ratio, 108
  Gas flow parameter curves, 115, 116
  Instrumentation, 108
  Jet thrust for subsonic flow, 108, 109
  Jet thrust for sonic flow, 109
  Jet velocity, 110
  Jet thrust parameter curves, 113, 114
  Sample calculations, 111, 112
  Thermocouple recovery factor, 110
Thrust horsepower required
  Climb, 74
  Level flight, 60

Thrust measurement, 106, 112, 117, 118
Torquemeter, 45
Trailing bomb, 22, 43
True airspeed determination, 32
  Data reduction, 32
  Data required, 32
Turbo-jet engine description, 101, 102
  See also jet propulsion

Universal rate of climb equation, 72
Universal rmp-speed polar — jet airplanes, 125
Universal speed-power polar
  Data reduction, 62
  Data required, 63
  Equation, 61
  Maximum speed determination, 65
  Polar, 61
Universal speed-thrust polar — jet airplanes, 125
  Alternate universal method, 125
  Equation, 124

Velocity of sound, 7, 8, 29
Von Karman's equation, 9

Weight — see gross weight
Whittle, 101
Whittle engine description, 101, 102
Whittle engine sketch, 101
Wind velocity
  Effect of wind gradient on climb, 71
  Effect on range, 85
  Effect on speed course calibration, 20, 21
  Effect on take-off, 78–80
  Measurement, 3